D0363587
UH?
HAVE THE MICE "SNOOKERED" KORKY'S GAME? TURN TO THE BACK OF THE BOOK!
£3.10

Printed and published in Great Britain by D. C. THOMSON & CO. LTD.,
185 Fleet Street, London EC4A 2HS.

ISBN 0 85116 411 0

BOOK
THE DANDY FUN TEAM REPORTING FOR DUTY, SIR!
STOMP!

Desperate DAN
...MEETS THE PRESIDENT
...AND I SWEAR TO BE LOYAL TO MY COUNTRY AND DO MY DUTY AT ALL TIMES...
SHUCKS! I'M THE PRESIDENT'S SPECIAL HELPER! WHAT AN HONOUR!
Back home—
YOU HELPIN' THE PRESIDENT! THAT'S PIE-IN-THE-SKY, DAN!
THE PHONE! IT MUST BE HIM!!!
RING!
THERE'S A TIDAL WAVE HEADING FOR SOUTHSHORE ZOO! TRY AND SAVE THE ANIMALS, DAN!
YES,MR PRESIDENT!
SHUCKS! I AIN'T GOT MUCH TIME!

Later —
THANKS FOR PUTTING THE ANIMALS UP HIGH, DAN!
DON'T MENTION IT!
ZOO
ZOO
NOW PLEASE GET 'EM DOWN AGAIN!
ZOO
Back home —
SAVIN' ANIMALS! MORE PIE-IN-THE-SKY STORIES, DAN!
RRRING!
PHONE AGAIN!
THERE'S A SPY LOOSE ON CACTUSVILLE AIRFORCE BASE, DAN!
I'LL ARREST 'IM, MR PRESIDENT!
PING!
THE SPY'S PHOTOGRAPHING OUR SECRET PLANES, DAN! GO IN AND GRAB HIM . . .
ON YER BIKE!
BUZZ OFF!
KEEP OUT
. . . BUT YOU'LL HAVE TO WEAR A BLINDFOLD! THE WHOLE PLACE IS TOP SECRET!
UH?

NOW WHERE IS HE?
USAF
HI-TECH
CHOP!
TOP SECRET SIGN— DO NOT READ THIS!
C'MERE, MR SPY!
CHOP!
MUGSKI!
I'LL GET 'IM!
CHOP!
WHAT'S THAT NOISE?
SHUCKSKI!!!
WHOOSH!
OUCHSKI!!!
SLAM!
THANKS, DAN!

YOU CAUGHT A SPY?!? MORE PIE-IN-THE-SKY, DAN!
I THINK I HEAR THE PHONE RINGIN'!
THE BLACKFOOT AND REDNOSE INDIAN TRIBES ARE AT WAR ON TOMAHAWK MOUNTAIN! BRING 'EM DOWN TO MEET THE PEACEMAKER, DAN!
WILL DO, MR PRES!
THEY SURE ARE AN ANGRY BUNCH!
WHUMP!
NOW CUT OUT ALL THAT FEUDIN'!
YOU GUYS ARE COMIN' DOWN THE MOUNTAIN WITH ME TO TALK TO THE RED INDIAN PEACEMAKER!
THAT PEACEMAKER WILL SURE HAVE A TOUGH JOB!

Fly with Dan Airways
WAAH!
MISSED!

180!
YOW!

...THEN THEY HAD A BATTLE ON THE WINGS...
RED INJUN BATTLES! MORE PIE-IN-THE-SKY, DAN!
COW PIE STORE
I'M FED UP OF AUNT AGGIE NOT BELIEVIN' ME! I'M GOIN' FOR A FEED!
OH, NO! THOSE PESKY MICE HAVE EATEN ALL MAH COW-PIES!
COW-PIE
COW-PI
MR PRESIDENT, NOW I NEED YOUR HELP, SIR!
Soon—
THE PRESIDENT SENT THOSE PLANES TO DELIVER SOMETHING TO ME!
MORE PIE-IN-THE-SKY, DAN!

COW-PIE
COW-PIE
YOU SAID IT, AUNTIE! PIE-IN-THE-SKY!

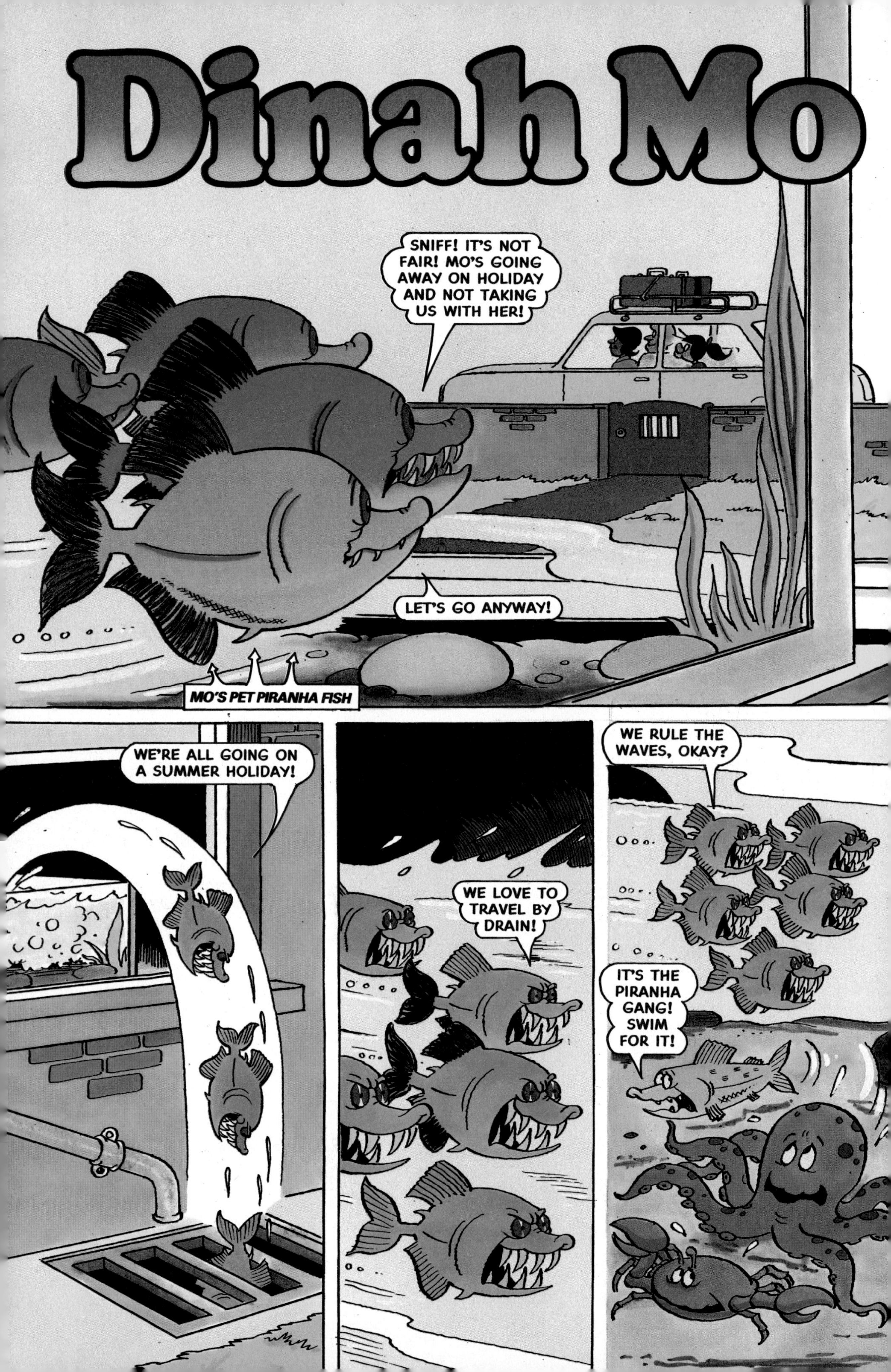
Dinah Mo
SNIFF! IT'S NOT FAIR! MO'S GOING AWAY ON HOLIDAY AND NOT TAKING US WITH HER!
LET'S GO ANYWAY!
MO'S PET PIRANHA FISH
WE'RE ALL GOING ON A SUMMER HOLIDAY!
WE LOVE TO TRAVEL BY DRAIN!
WE RULE THE WAVES, OKAY?
IT'S THE PIRANHA GANG! SWIM FOR IT!

Meanwhile —
I'M MISSING MY PET PIRANHA FISH! WISH THEY WERE HERE!
EH? HE'S MOVING FASTER THAN ME!
SNAP SNAP
HOLIDAY CAMP
THEY ARE HERE!
I'VE GOT A BITE . . . I THINK!
CHOMP! CHOMP!
HELP! IT'S THEM THAT HAVE THE BITE!
SNAP! CRUNCH!
WH-WHAT'S THAT NOISE?
A BIT ON THE LOUD SIDE FOR WOODWORM!
CHEW! CRUNCH! CHOMP! CHEW!
ABANDON BOAT!
CHOMP! CHOMP!

IS THAT ALL THE PIRANHA FISH ROUNDED UP, MO?
THERE'S ONE TO COME...
YAH! WHAT BIT ME?
BONK
GENTS→
SNAP
BITE
...BUT I THINK IT TOOK A WRONG TURNING!
WE'LL HAVE TO SHELTER IN THE LEISURE COMPLEX!
EVERYONE'S CROWDING IN HERE! WE WON'T GET NEAR THE POOL!
SWIMMING POOL
IDEA
YOUR FISH HAVE THEIR USES AFTER ALL, MO!
GRR!
SNARL!
SNAP!

A DAY IN THE LIFE OF
BULLY BEEF
with CHIPS
YAWN
Get up.
R-R-RING
THUMP
Go to school.
ERK! IT'S BEEFY!
Hit someone — anyone . . .
SCHOOL
BIFF
Bully someone — anyone.
TUG!
YEEK!
Have lunch.
STUFF!

Have someone else's lunch.
Leave school before anyone else.
SCHOOL
Play with a football — anyone's football.
Beat up one person in particular — CHIPS!
SPORTS
I'M PREPARED FOR YOU, BEEFY!
SPORTS
Finally, I see a doctor — any doctor!
SURGERY
SURGERY
OH, NO! NOT YOU AGAIN!
AREA MEDICAL CENTRE

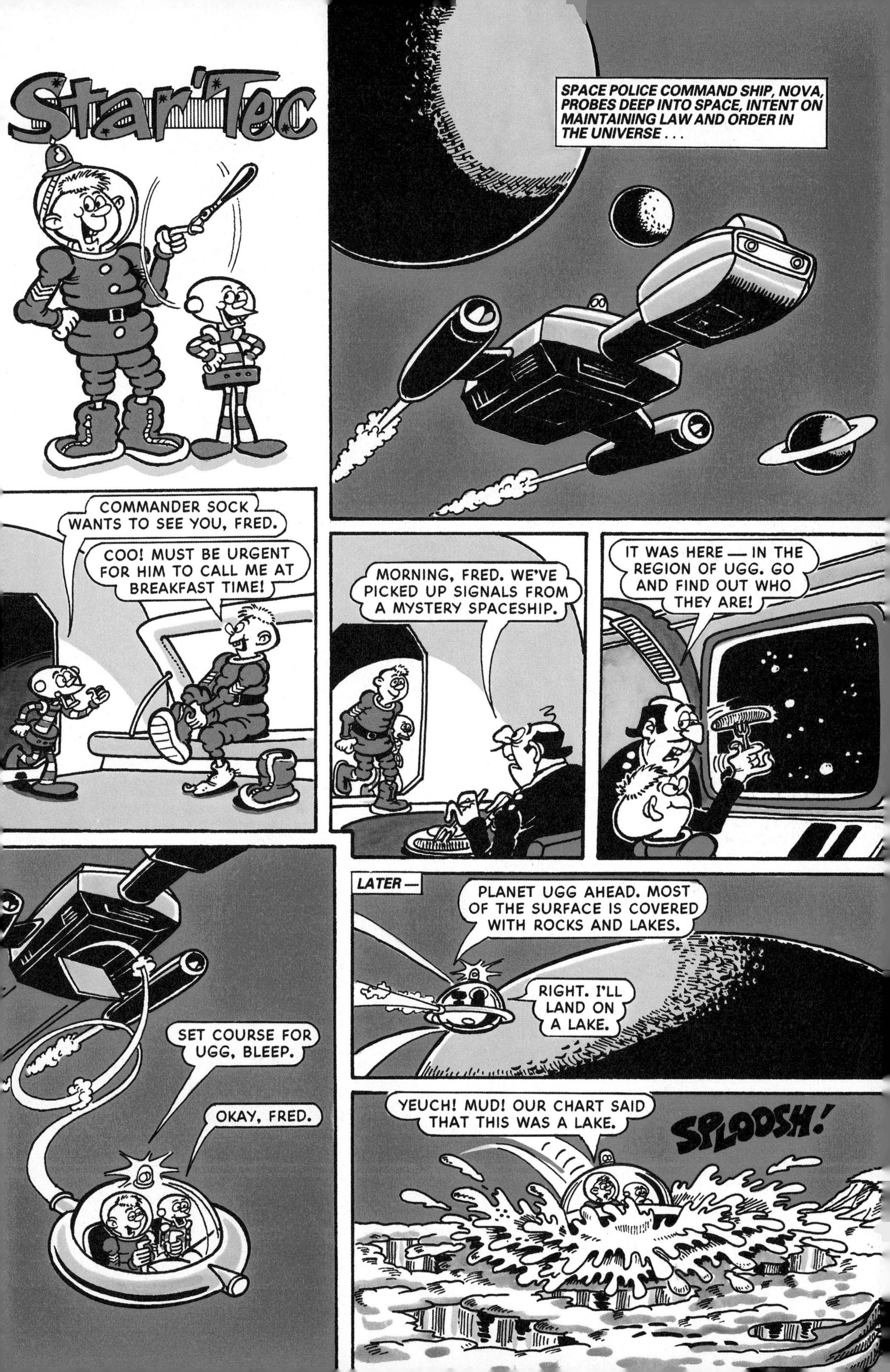
Star'Tec
SPACE POLICE COMMAND SHIP, NOVA, PROBES DEEP INTO SPACE, INTENT ON MAINTAINING LAW AND ORDER IN THE UNIVERSE . . .
COMMANDER SOCK WANTS TO SEE YOU, FRED.
COO! MUST BE URGENT FOR HIM TO CALL ME AT BREAKFAST TIME!
MORNING, FRED. WE'VE PICKED UP SIGNALS FROM A MYSTERY SPACESHIP.
IT WAS HERE — IN THE REGION OF UGG. GO AND FIND OUT WHO THEY ARE!
SET COURSE FOR UGG, BLEEP.
OKAY, FRED.
LATER —
PLANET UGG AHEAD. MOST OF THE SURFACE IS COVERED WITH ROCKS AND LAKES.
RIGHT. I'LL LAND ON A LAKE.
YEUCH! MUD! OUR CHART SAID THAT THIS WAS A LAKE.
SPLOOSH!

WHAT'S HAPPENED TO THE LAKE? HOW CAN WE GET ASHORE?
THE LAKE HAS BEEN STOLEN BY A SPACESHIP FROM THE PLANET WEIRD.
TIME TO TRANSFORM.
GOOD OLD BLEEP. HE'S TRANSFORMING INTO A MINI-HELICOPTER.
COMING IN TO LAND. STAND CLEAR.
THE WEIRDOS SUCKED UP ALL OUR LAKES AND SEAS AND TURNED THEM INTO LITTLE CAPSULES. THEY DROPPED THESE!
HMM. WONDER WHAT HAPPENS IF YOU PRICK IT WITH A PIN.
GLUG!
THAT'S CLEVER — THEY CONCENTRATE WHOLE LAKES INTO LITTLE CAPSULES.
ER... OUR SPACESHIP IS STUCK IN THE MUD. YOU DON'T HAVE A CRANE ON YOU, BY ANY CHANCE?
A CRANE? 'COURSE I DO.
PHEEP!

WHAT? OH, YES, OF COURSE — A CRANE BIRD.
HERE HE IS.
HE DOES ALL THE HEAVY LIFTING FOR US.
SO —
THE COMPUTER SAYS THAT THE PLANET WEIRD IS ALMOST OUT OF WATER — WATER IS EVEN MORE VALUABLE THAN GOLD THERE, BLEEP!
NO WONDER THE WEIRDOS ARE PINCHING OTHER PEOPLE'S WATER.
THE WEIRDO'S SHIP.
WE'VE JUST IDENTIFIED A RADAR SIGNAL, COMMANDER WALLY — WE ARE BEING FOLLOWED BY A SPACE POLICE VEHICLE.
THAT MEANS JUST ONE THING — THE COPS KNOW WHAT WE'RE UP TO . . .
. . . SO I WANT THEM ELIMINATED.
YES, COMMANDER.
SO A SPACE FIGHTER IS LAUNCHED —
SOON —
THE WEIRDO SHIP IS STRAIGHT AHEAD BUT A NEW BLIP HAS APPEARED ON THE RADAR BEHIND US.
WHAT BLIP, BLEEP?

YOWCH! THAT BLIP!
BOOF!
OO-ER! WE'VE GOT ROCKET TROUBLE. I'LL LAND ON THIS PLANET.
PHUTT! PHUTT!
PHUTT!
PHEW! A BIT OF A BUMPY LANDIN', BUT WE'VE MADE IT.
NO REAL DAMAGE — I'LL SOON FIX IT!
AT LAST — THE SPACE POLICE. YOU'RE JUST IN TIME...
...THE NIBBLERS HAVE TAKEN A FANCY TO OUR BUILDINGS.
NIBBLE!
NIBBLE!
NIBBLE!
WHAT ARE NIBBLERS?
NIBBLE!
NIBBLE!
AAIEE!
ER... THESE ARE NIBBLERS.
CHOMP! CHOMP!
I HOPE MY BUBBLE-GUM DIDN'T GET WET.
BUBBLE GUM?
HEY! WHAT'S THE IDEA?
THEY'RE CURIOUS ABOUT YOUR BOOTS.
CHOMP! CHOMP!
HO! HO! THEY LIKE BUBBLE-GUM! WE'LL START A BUBBLE-GUM FACTORY!
HO! HO! THIS'LL STOP THE LITTLE BLIGHTERS NIBBLING.

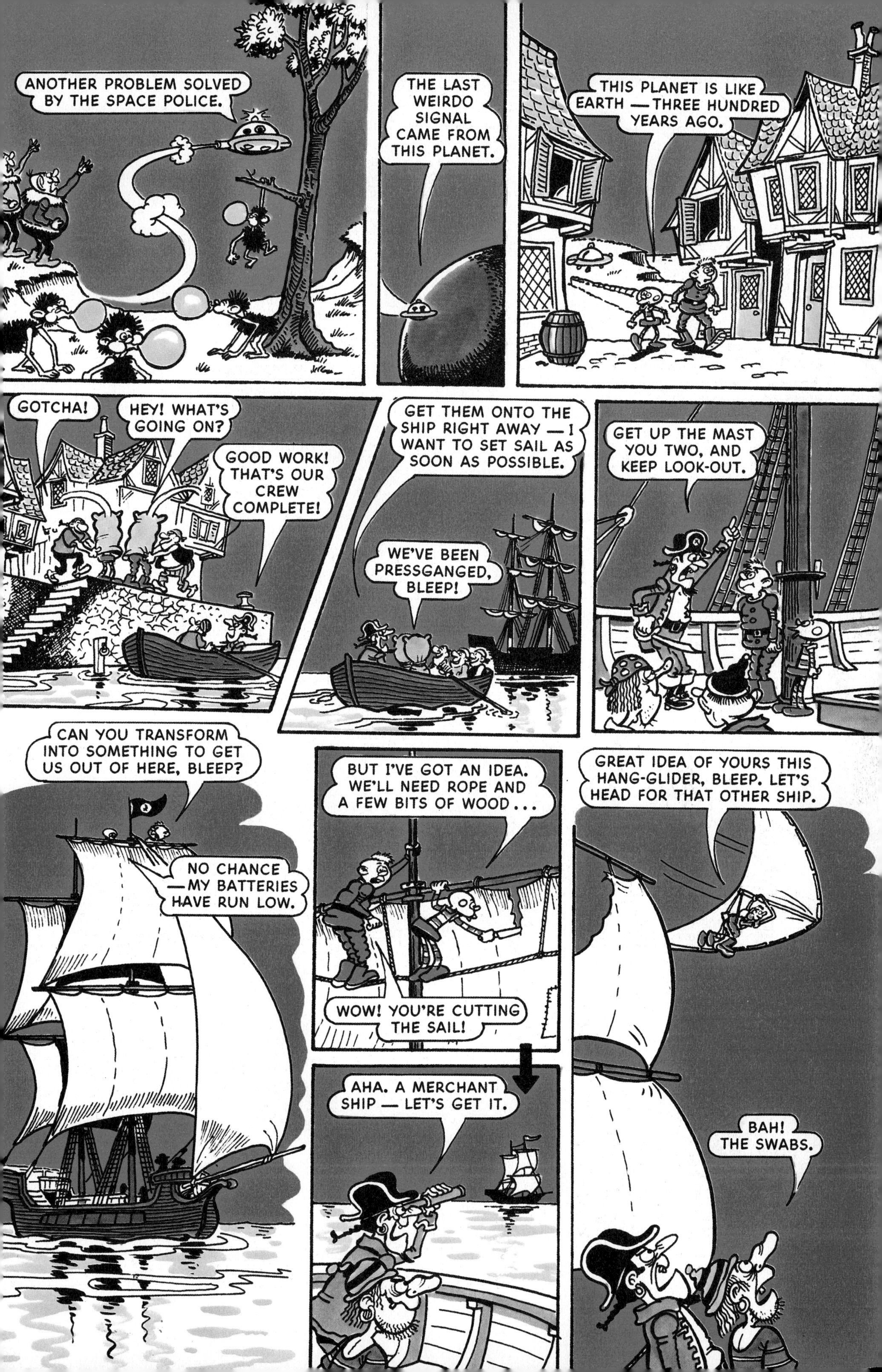
ANOTHER PROBLEM SOLVED BY THE SPACE POLICE.
THE LAST WEIRDO SIGNAL CAME FROM THIS PLANET.
THIS PLANET IS LIKE EARTH — THREE HUNDRED YEARS AGO.
GOTCHA!
HEY! WHAT'S GOING ON?
GOOD WORK! THAT'S OUR CREW COMPLETE!
GET THEM ONTO THE SHIP RIGHT AWAY — I WANT TO SET SAIL AS SOON AS POSSIBLE.
WE'VE BEEN PRESSGANGED, BLEEP!
GET UP THE MAST YOU TWO, AND KEEP LOOK-OUT.
CAN YOU TRANSFORM INTO SOMETHING TO GET US OUT OF HERE, BLEEP?
NO CHANCE —MY BATTERIES HAVE RUN LOW.
BUT I'VE GOT AN IDEA. WE'LL NEED ROPE AND A FEW BITS OF WOOD...
WOW! YOU'RE CUTTING THE SAIL!
AHA. A MERCHANT SHIP — LET'S GET IT.
GREAT IDEA OF YOURS THIS HANG-GLIDER, BLEEP. LET'S HEAD FOR THAT OTHER SHIP.
BAH! THE SWABS.

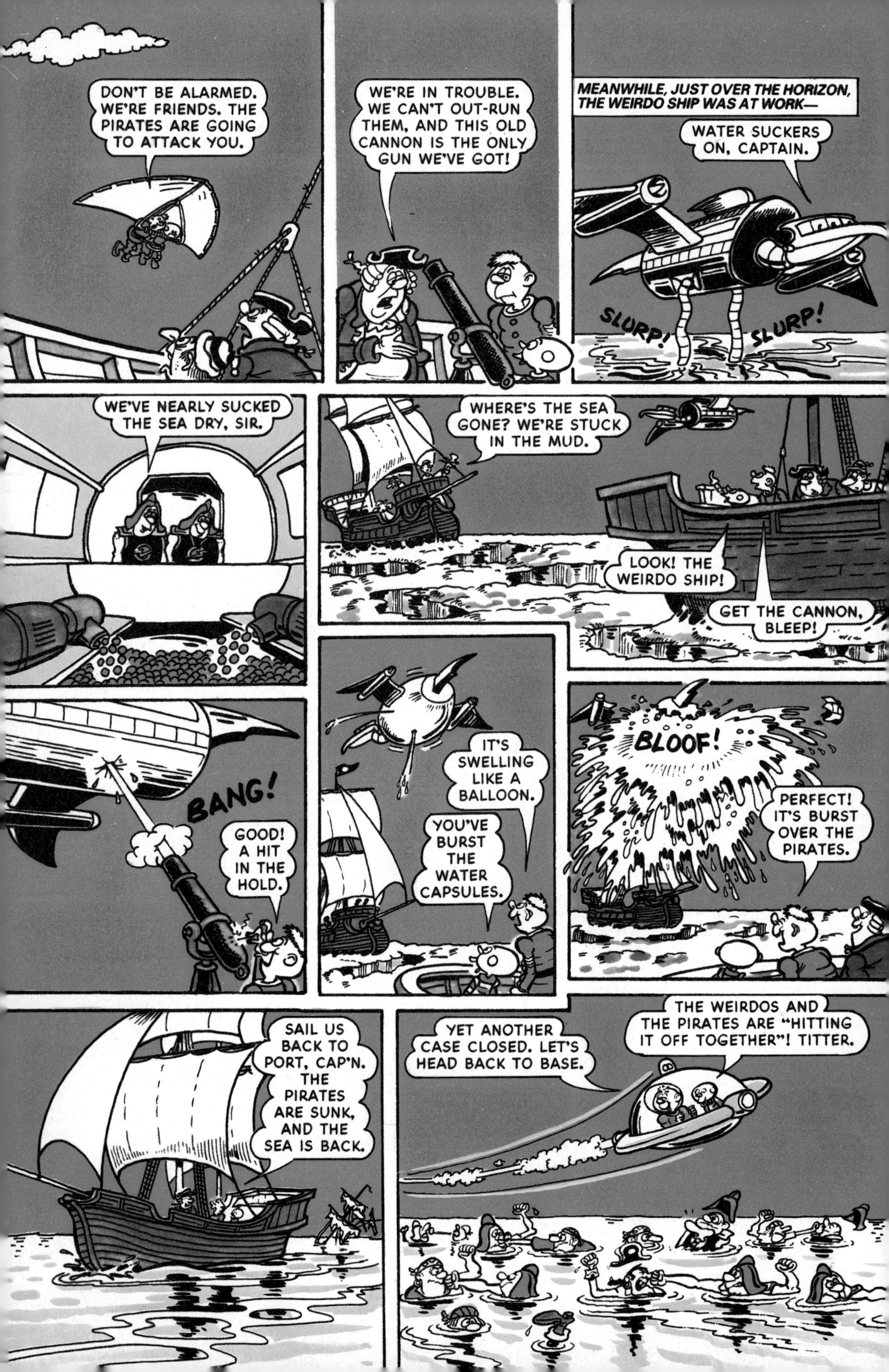

DON'T BE ALARMED. WE'RE FRIENDS. THE PIRATES ARE GOING TO ATTACK YOU.
WE'RE IN TROUBLE. WE CAN'T OUT-RUN THEM, AND THIS OLD CANNON IS THE ONLY GUN WE'VE GOT!
MEANWHILE, JUST OVER THE HORIZON, THE WEIRDO SHIP WAS AT WORK—
WATER SUCKERS ON, CAPTAIN.
SLURP! SLURP!
WE'VE NEARLY SUCKED THE SEA DRY, SIR.
WHERE'S THE SEA GONE? WE'RE STUCK IN THE MUD.
LOOK! THE WEIRDO SHIP!
GET THE CANNON, BLEEP!
BANG!
GOOD! A HIT IN THE HOLD.
IT'S SWELLING LIKE A BALLOON.
YOU'VE BURST THE WATER CAPSULES.
BLOOF!
PERFECT! IT'S BURST OVER THE PIRATES.
SAIL US BACK TO PORT, CAP'N. THE PIRATES ARE SUNK, AND THE SEA IS BACK.
YET ANOTHER CASE CLOSED. LET'S HEAD BACK TO BASE.
THE WEIRDOS AND THE PIRATES ARE "HITTING IT OFF TOGETHER"! TITTER.

Mutt AND Moggy
OH, JOY! I GOTTA BONE! YER CAN HAVE LOTSA LAUGHS WIV A BONE!
FOR INSTANCE — THIS!
BOP!
YOWLLLLLL!
GOOD! I PREFER A MOVIN' TARGET!
FORE!
WAAH!
PHUNG!
SHUNK!
YOU SHOULDN'T HAVE DONE THAT, MUTT — FOR THAT, I'M GONNA . . .
WOTTAGIGGLE!
DROP!
SHTUMB!
HARDYHARHAR!

...F-FLATTEN Y-Y-YOU!
SEE? SEE? HEE! HEE! TOLD YER YOU COULD HAVE LOTSA LAUGHS WIV A BONE!
PLENTY OF FIZZY POP WILL SOON BLOW ME BACK INTO SHAPE!
EXTRA-FIZZY POP
Soon—
HIC! I TH-THINK I OVERDID THE FIZZY POP, BUT NOT T'WORRY...
...I'M STILL IN GOOD ENOUGH SHAPE TO BEAT UP MUTT — PUT 'EM UP, DAWG!
BACK FOR MORE, HMM?
YER A REAL GLUTTON FOR PUNISHMENT, MOGGY!
OW!
CRUNCH!
NOW, IF I THUMP THIS OTHER PAW, ALSO, TOO, AS WELL...
BOUNCE!
...HE HASN'T GOT A LEG TO STAND ON! YES, YER CAN HAVE LOTS AN' LOTS OF LAUGHS WIV A BONE, FOLKS!

ONLY BABIES SUCK THEIR PAWS!
NO — DON'T TAKE ME...
... PAWS OUT OF ME MOUF! HELP!
BLAART!
Later —
I'LL HAVE MORE LAUGHS WIV ME BONE AFTER NOSH!
THAT'S WOT HE THINKS!
After nosh —
OI! WHERE'S ME BONE, POOZYCAT?
KEEP YER SKIN ON — IT'S OVER THERE — PROPPED AGAINST THE SHED DOOR!
WHIMPER!
RUMBLE!
AN', IF YOU THINK BONES ARE SUCH FUN, THINK OF THE LAUGHS YOU'LL HAVE...
CLUNG! CHUNG! CRUNCH!
T-TRAPPED BY ME OWN B-BONE!
... GETTIN' ALL YOUR BONES PLASTERED!

IF YOU'RE LONELY, DAN, WHY NOT GO ALONG TO THE LOCAL DANCE AND MEET A NICE GIRL?
I'LL GIVE IT A TRY, AUNT AGGIE!
TONIGHT ROCK 'N' ROLL DANCE
ROCK 'N' ROLL DANCIN'! I COULD DO THAT!
Desperate DAN
JUST THROW THE GALS INTO THE AIR! YAHOO!
ZOOM!
STOMP! STOMP!
I'VE RUN OUTTA DANCIN' PARTNERS!
AND SO HAVE WE! BIG GALOOT!

THERE'S THERESA GREEN, MY CHILDHOOD SWEETHEART!
I'LL REMIND HER OF THE TRICKS I USED TO DO AT SCHOOL!
ARE YOU IMPRESSED, THERESA?
NO!
AND NEITHER'S GRANNY SMITH!
ULP! DON'T REMEMBER TOSSIN' HER UP THERE!
ANYWAY, I ALREADY HAVE A BOYFRIEND, AND HE CAN HOLD UP THREE BUSES, FOUR TRUCKS AND TEN CARS WITH ONE HAND!
UH? IS HE CONAN THE LIBRARIAN OR SOMETHIN'?
AW, SHUCKS!
NO! HE'S A TRAFFIC COP! SEE HOW HE HOLDS UP THE TRAFFIC WITH ONE HAND!
COMPUTA DATING COMPANY
THIS IS MY LAST CHANCE! MAYBE A COMPUTER CAN FIND ME A GIRLFRIEND!
FILL IN THIS FORM PLEASE!

# COMPUTA DATE COMPANY APPLICATION FORM

NAME : .......... Desperate Dan
ADDRESS : ....... Cactusville, Texas.
BORN : .......... Yup!
MALE OR FEMALE ... Yup!
EYES : .............. Two
WEIGHT : ............. 250 Kilos before lunch, 275 Kilos after lunch.
HEIGHT : ............. One inch taller than my front door.
HOBBY : .............. Woodwork-mainly repairing the top of my front door.
FAVOURITE DISH : .......... Cowpie.
LEAST FAVOURITE DISH : ...... Empty Cow-pie dish.
FAVOURITE DRINK : ......... Owl hoot juice.
FAVOURITE NEWSPAPER : ..... The Texas Times. It's thick and keeps the fish 'n' chips warm.
NICKNAME : .............. "HOTLIPS" - especially after eatin' curried cow-pie.
ARE YOU (✓ TICK) .......... ① VERY CLEVER ② QUITE CLEVER ③ SLIGHTLY CLEVER ?
✓ Duh! I can't understand the question!
PETS : ................. Two skunks, a wildcat and a racoon. Well, that's what I found in mah bed when I woke up this morning.
SPECIAL DISLIKES : ........ Eating between meals.
SPECIAL LIKES : ........... Having at least 12 meals a day.
GENERAL LIKES : .......... General Patton, General Custer and General Store.
FAVOURITE THING ON TV : .... The big bowl of fruit that Aunt Aggie keeps on top of our TV.
TYPE OF FEMALE YOU'D LIKE TO MEET : .......... Tall with soft brown hair and long nails. Must love the outdoors.

SIGN .......... Desperate Dan

CALL BACK LATER AND I'LL HAVE A DATE FOR YOU!
COMPUTER
I'LL NEED A HAIRCUT AND SHAVE FIRST!
At the Indian Reservation —
BOOT!
CHOP!
SURE BEATS PAYIN' A BARBER!
TIME FOR A SHAVE NOW!
USAF
15
IT TAKES A LOT TO SHIFT MAH TOUGH STUBBLE!
WE ONLY HAVE ONE TALL FEMALE WITH SOFT BROWN HAIR, LONG NAILS AND A LOVE OF THE OUTDOORS!
LET'S MEET HER!

HERE SHE IS!
A BEAR?!?
WELL SHE DOES FIT YOUR REQUIREMENTS!
ER, BUT IT LOOKS AS IF YOU DON'T FIT HER DESCRIPTION, DAN, AFTER YOUR SHAVE AND HAIRCUT!
TYPE OF MALE YOU'D LIKE TO MEET
HAIRY
SORRY I COULDN'T HELP YOU!
HUH! NO ONE LOVES ME, NOT EVEN A BEAR!
Reader's voice.
I KNOW WHO LOVES YOU, DAN!
EH? WHO?
A MILLION DANDY READERS, THAT'S WHO!
I FORGOT ABOUT ALL YOU GUYS AN' GALS OUT THERE! IT'S GREAT TO BE LOVED!

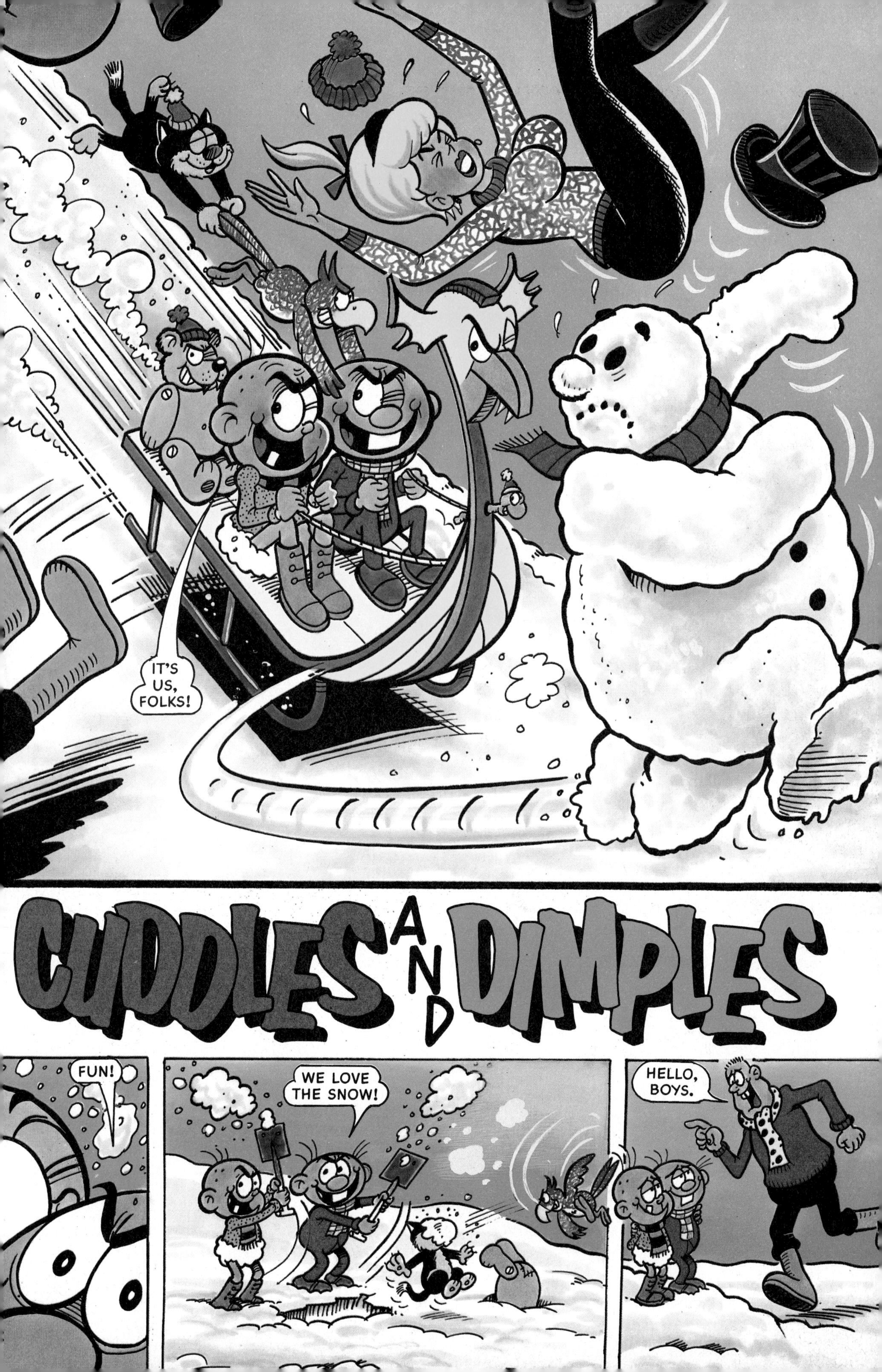
IT'S US, FOLKS!
CUDDLES AND DIMPLES
FUN!
WE LOVE THE SNOW!
HELLO, BOYS.

FLUMP!
WAAAAH!
DEEP, INNIT?
YEP.
WE PLAY WIV SNOW. WE MAKE —
SPLAT! SPLAT! SPLAT!
— A SNOWMAN!

HIM FROZEN IN PLACE!
HELP ME GET DAD OUT OF THE ICE.
WE GO SLEDGIN'.
NO. WE'LL GO SKATING ON THE POND.

WE SKATE ROUND EDGE.
SPLOSH!

I NEED HEATED UP.
BAG OF HOT CHESTNUTS, PLEASE.
WE HEAT YOU UP.
ARGH!
OWW! I'M TOO HOT!
IN THIS WEATHER?
AHH! THANKS, MUM! OKAY, BOYS — WE'LL GO SLEDGING.
Y'KNOW, THIS IS FUN!

WAH!
EEK!
ZOOM!
GANGWAY!
THEY DON'T SEE THE BOULDER!
DIVE! DIVE! DIVE!

Brassneck
WHICH HEAD SHOULD I WEAR TODAY, CHARLEY?
THUG
EGG HEAD
PUNK
BABY
FRANKIE
P.M.
POSER
MOLE
HEAD HEAD
EAGLE EYES
DAN
SWIMMER
PRINCE
VAMPIRE
PILOT
BRASSNECK HAS LOTS OF FUN CHANGING HEADS. HE'S GIVEN ME SOME LAUGHS TOO.
THE
WIN A DESPERATE DAN T-SHIRT

BRASSNECK WANTED TO SCARE OUR PALS WITH HIS VAMPIRE HEAD.
CACKLE! HISS!
SIGH!
BUT VAMPIRES ONLY COME OUT AT MIDNIGHT AND NONE OF OUR PALS ARE AROUND THEN.

BRASSNECK CAN SEE FOR MILES WITH HIS EAGLE HEAD.
AWK!
CHIRP!
BUT HE BUILT AN EYRIE ON THE SOFA. WHAT A BIRD-BRAIN!

HO! HO! THAT'S A GOOD ONE! THAT'S THE FUNNIEST HEAD YET.
WHAT?
YOU CHEEKY BALLOON! THIS IS MY OWN NORMAL HEAD! GRR!
RELAX, MY OLD METAL MATE. I WAS ONLY PULLING YOUR LEG!

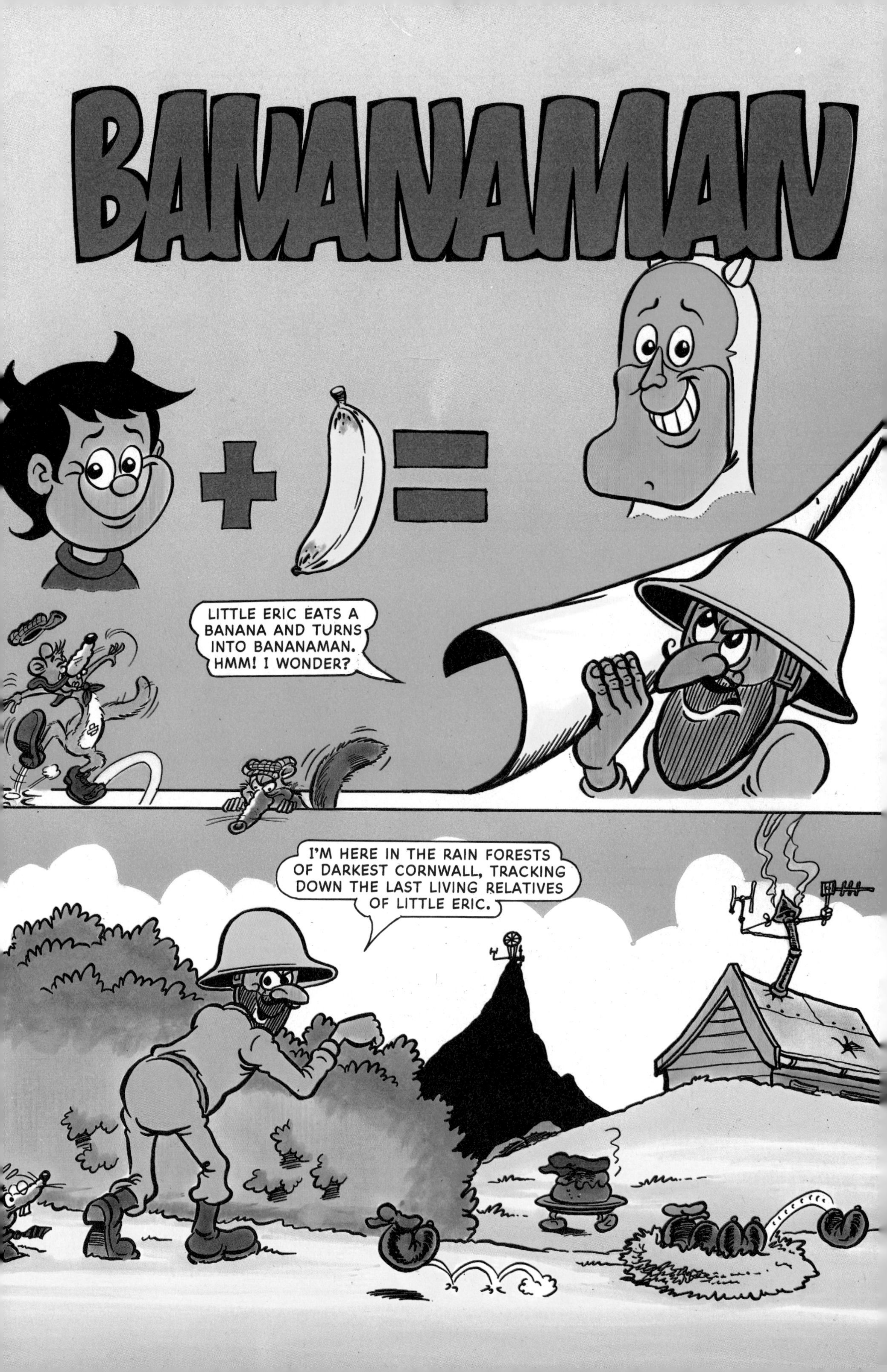
BANANAMAN
LITTLE ERIC EATS A BANANA AND TURNS INTO BANANAMAN. HMM! I WONDER?
I'M HERE IN THE RAIN FORESTS OF DARKEST CORNWALL, TRACKING DOWN THE LAST LIVING RELATIVES OF LITTLE ERIC.

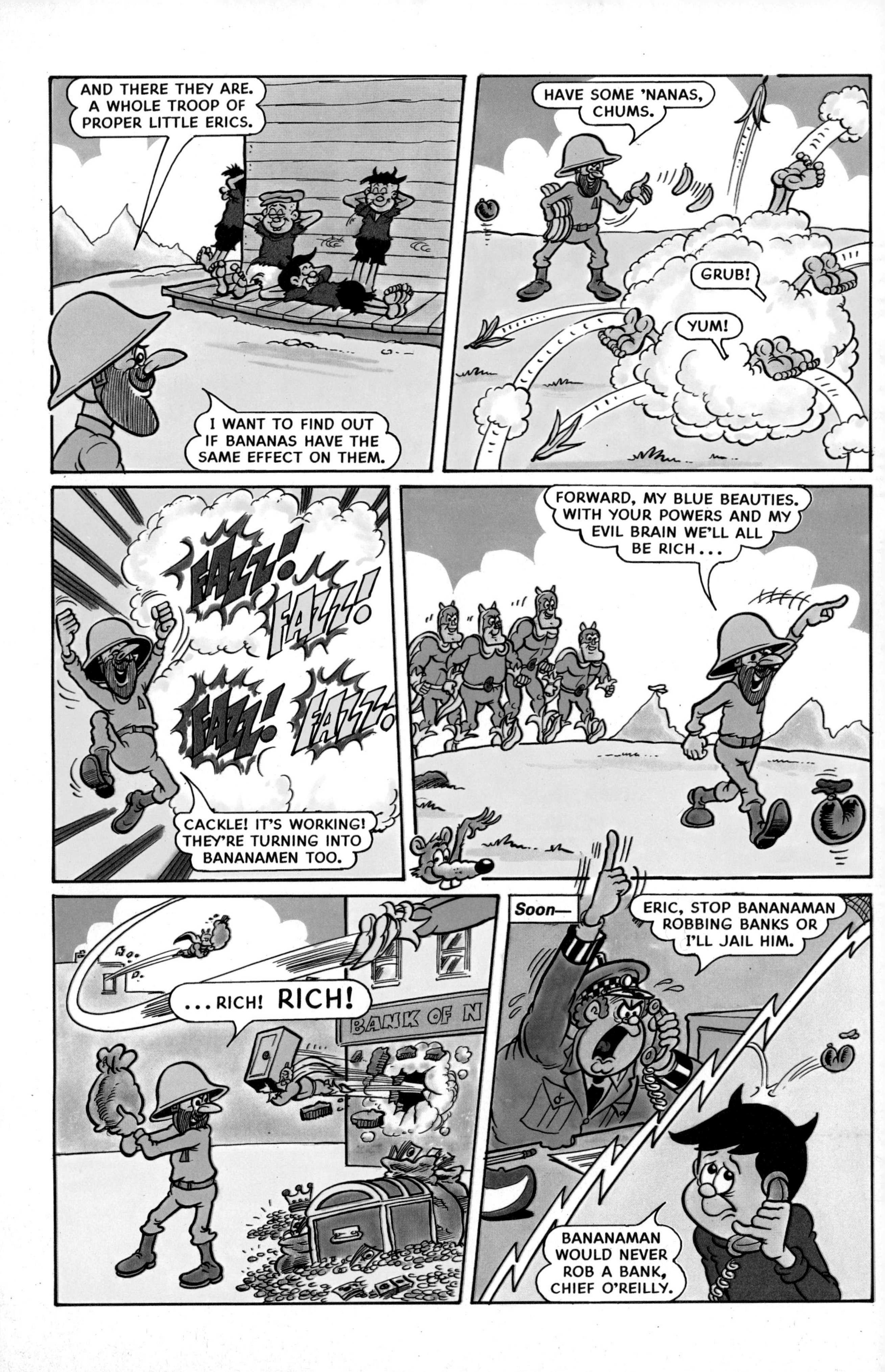
AND THERE THEY ARE. A WHOLE TROOP OF PROPER LITTLE ERICS.
I WANT TO FIND OUT IF BANANAS HAVE THE SAME EFFECT ON THEM.
HAVE SOME 'NANAS, CHUMS.
GRUB!
YUM!
FAZZ!
FAZZ!
FAZZ!
FAZZ!
CACKLE! IT'S WORKING! THEY'RE TURNING INTO BANANAMEN TOO.
FORWARD, MY BLUE BEAUTIES. WITH YOUR POWERS AND MY EVIL BRAIN WE'LL ALL BE RICH . . .
. . . RICH! RICH!
BANK OF N
Soon—
ERIC, STOP BANANAMAN ROBBING BANKS OR I'LL JAIL HIM.
BANANAMAN WOULD NEVER ROB A BANK, CHIEF O'REILLY.

STILL, I'LL EAT A 'NANA AND CHECK.
FAZZOOM!
NOPE! I'VE NOT ROBBED A BANK — LOOK, I'M BROKE.
SOMETHING FUNNY IS GOING ON — I'VE A FEELING I'M BEING FOLLOWED.
IT'S ME!
NO — IT'S US! YOUR COUSINS, BANANAMAN.
LET ME INTRODUCE YOU TO COUSIN ROGER'S FIST...
...NIGEL'S KNEE...
...HORACE'S HEAD!
FOR THE SAKE OF MY GREY HAIRED OLD BANANAGRAN, I MUST STOP THOSE NAUGHTY COUSINS.
MY COUSINS COME FROM CORNWALL.
AND WE ALL KNOW WHAT CORNISH LADS LIKE TO EAT... YORKSHIRE PUDDINGS!
Shortly—
HAVE ANOTHER 'NANA, MEN. KEEP YOUR STRENGTH UP.

SHRIEK!
YOUR DEAR COUSIN HAS BROUGHT YOU SOME REAL EATS — YORKSHIRE PUDS!
DON'T LISTEN TO HIM! EAT YOUR 'NANAS!
YUM!
YUM!
YUM!
GRR! I'LL SET MY BANANA BUNCH ON YOU!
TRY IT, GENERAL.
HO! HO! THAT FAT BUNCH CAN'T FLY ANYWHERE.
ATTACK! ATTACK HIM, MEN!

BUT YOU CAN FLY, GENERAL BLIGHT.
NO! NO! I'VE ALWAYS BEEN A GOOD BOY! I DON'T WANT TO FLY!
WE HAVE LIFT-OFF!
WOO-HOO-HOO!
BOFF!
OOPS! SORRY, BLIGHT. I MISSED THE JAIL DOOR!
URF!
THE NICK
BLIGHT IS GONE SO YOU CAN BE HONEST CITIZENS AGAIN, COUSINS.
BUT HOW ARE WE GOING TO MAKE MONEY NOW?
IT SO HAPPENS I HAVE A BANANAPLAN.
SINGE YOUR BLUE BOTTYS BY THE BRAZIER, BOYS.

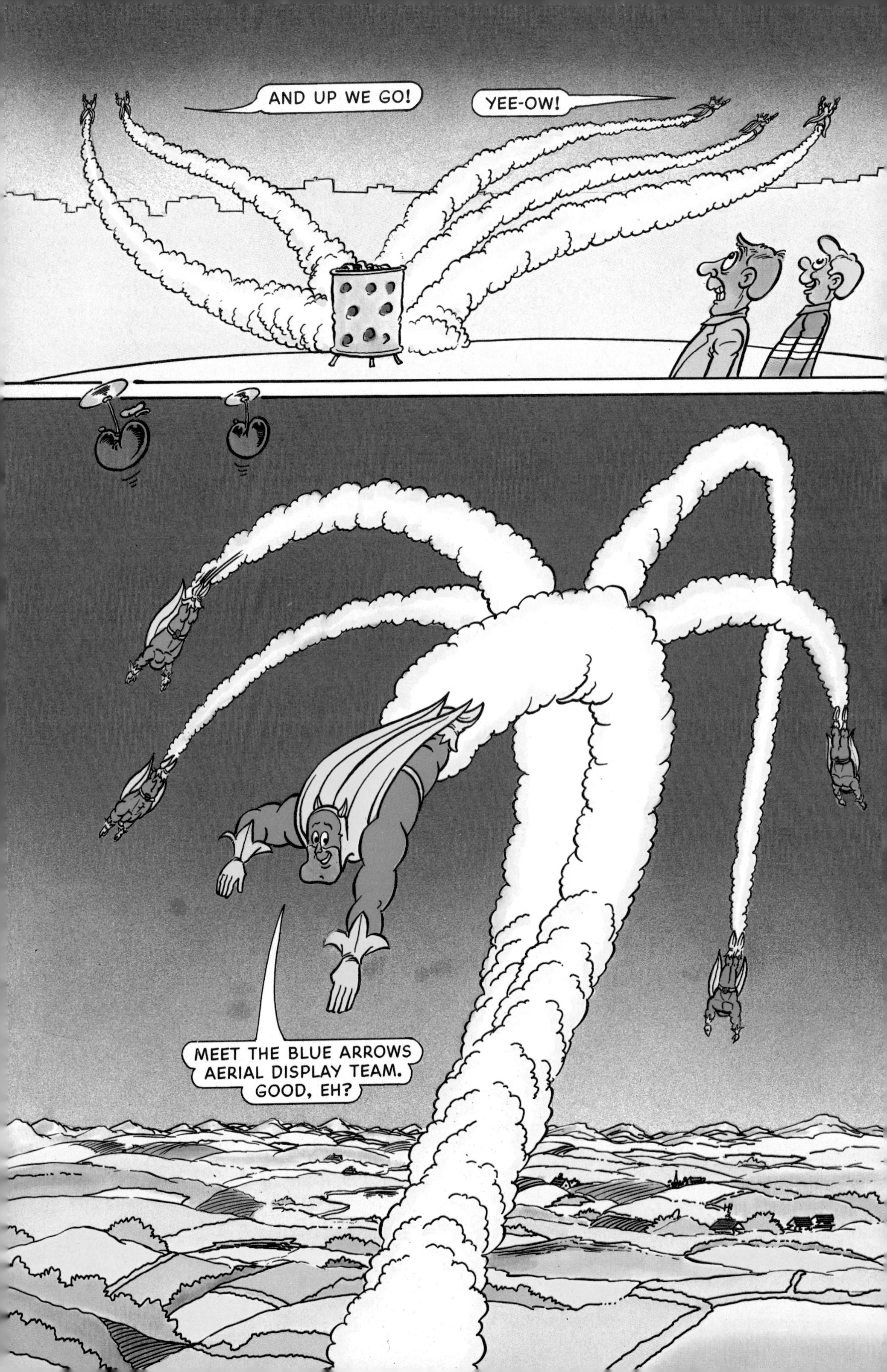
AND UP WE GO!
YEE-OW!
MEET THE BLUE ARROWS AERIAL DISPLAY TEAM. GOOD, EH?

THE SMASHER
GENTLE PROD!
YOU SMASH EVERYTHING YOU TOUCH!
MEANWHILE...
IT GIVES ME PLEASURE TO DEMOLISH, AT LONG LAST, OLD SMOKEY STACK.
BRITISH INDUSTRY LTD.
BAH! IT WON'T COME DOWN! REMOVE THE EXPLOSIVES, AND I'LL GET A REAL DEMOLITION EXPERT!
So—
OF COURSE I'LL HELP! I'LL GET MY SPECIAL EQUIPMENT.
VROOM!

WHACK!
BOOT!
SWIPE!
BAH! NOTHING'S BROKEN IT! I'M BUSHED!
RUMBLE!
WHOOPS! I'VE BROUGHT IT DOWN, AT LAST!
WELL DONE, SMASHER! I'LL TAKE YOU HOME. NEXT LEFT?
RIGHT!
RIGHT? OKAY!
OH, NO! WE'RE GOING DIFFERENT WAYS!
SNAP!
CRASH!
WAAAAH!
MY BEAUTIFUL BIKE!
WELL, WHAT DOES HE EXPECT WITH ME AROUND?

KORKY THE CAT
HEY! LOOK—UNCLE KORKY WANTS TO PLAY . . .
. . . LEAPFROG!
YIKE!
OVER WE GO!
SPLOT!
DON'T WORRY! WE'LL SOON PULL YOU FREE, UNCLE KORKY!

PLOP!
SPLUT!
YOU LOT STOP BOTHERIN' ME — I'M TRYIN' TO PLANT THINGS — UNDERSTAND?
UNCLE KORKY DOESN'T WANT TO PLAY — SO WE'LL JUST HAVE A GAME OF FOOTBALL!
FINISHED DIGGIN' — NOW I CAN START PLANTING!
OOPS! MISSED!

WHUMP!
THAT DOES IT!
WOW! THAT'S A DEEP HOLE — WONDER WHAT UNCLE KORKY'S GOIN' TO PLANT IN HERE?
NOW WE KNOW — US!
I'LL PULL YOU UP WHEN I FINISH PLANTING — OR MAYBE I'LL WAIT TILL SPRING! SNIGGER!

DINAH MO
ROARRR!!!
POUND!
GNNNGH!!!
YAAAAA!!!
SOB!
FLOP!
HOW DID I DO?
THREE PERFECT TENS, MO! YOUR PERFORMANCE WAS BRILL!
10
10
10
JUDGES
I'LL TRY IT OUT ON DAD IF HE WON'T BUY ME BOXING GLOVES!

CAN I HAVE A PAIR OF BOXING GLOVES, DAD?
NO!
ER, CHANGED YOUR MIND, YET?
I WAS OUT GARDENING AND SAW WHAT YOU AND YOUR PALS WERE UP TO THROUGH THE WINDOW!
NO
ULP!
GET YOUR BOXING GLOVES, MO?
GLOOM!
NO! BUT EVEN WORSE...
...DAD LIKED MY PERFORMANCE SO MUCH, HE'S SENT ME TO DRAMA CLASSES!
DRAMA SCHOOL
IS THIS AN ACTING STUDENT I SEE BEFORE ME?

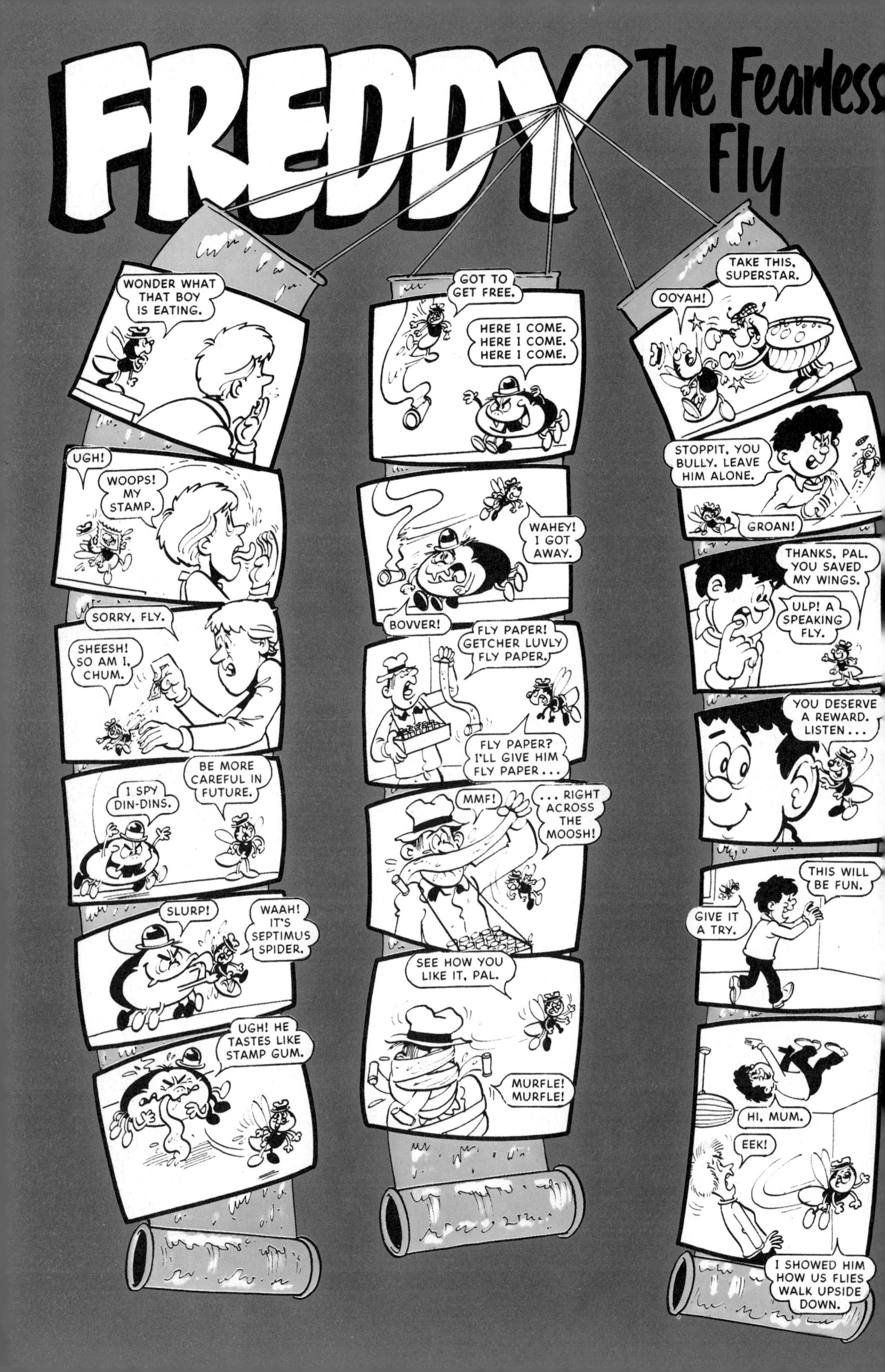
FREDDY The Fearless Fly
WONDER WHAT THAT BOY IS EATING.
UGH!
WOOPS! MY STAMP.
SORRY, FLY.
SHEESH! SO AM I, CHUM.
BE MORE CAREFUL IN FUTURE.
I SPY DIN-DINS.
SLURP!
WAAH! IT'S SEPTIMUS SPIDER.
UGH! HE TASTES LIKE STAMP GUM.
GOT TO GET FREE.
HERE I COME. HERE I COME. HERE I COME.
WAHEY! I GOT AWAY.
BOVVER!
FLY PAPER! GETCHER LUVLY FLY PAPER.
FLY PAPER? I'LL GIVE HIM FLY PAPER...
MMF!
... RIGHT ACROSS THE MOOSH!
SEE HOW YOU LIKE IT, PAL.
MURFLE! MURFLE!
TAKE THIS, SUPERSTAR.
OOYAH!
STOPPIT, YOU BULLY. LEAVE HIM ALONE.
GROAN!
THANKS, PAL. YOU SAVED MY WINGS.
ULP! A SPEAKING FLY.
YOU DESERVE A REWARD. LISTEN...
THIS WILL BE FUN.
GIVE IT A TRY.
HI, MUM.
EEK!
I SHOWED HIM HOW US FLIES WALK UPSIDE DOWN.

CORPORAL CLOTT
SQUEAK! BLUBBLE!
CLOTT! YOU'VE BEEN PLAYING THE BUGLE IN THE BATH AGAIN.
HANDEL'S WATER MUSIC, SIR.
HE BOYS FROM THE ARMY CADET FORCE ARE VISITING THE CAMP. I WANT YOU TO GIVE THEM SOME TRAINING, CLOTT.
YES, SIR, COLONEL GRÜMBLY.
FIRST THING I'M GOING TO SHOW YOU IS HOW TO SALUTE.
BIG DEAL!

BET YOU CAN'T SALUTE AND HOLD THIS CLUB AT THE SAME TIME.
'COURSE I CAN.
SEE... OUCH!
CLONK!
HA! HA! WHAT A NIT!
NEXT IS SURVIVAL TRAINING. GO FIND SOMETHING FOR YOUR LUNCH FROM THE LAND.
RUB! RUB!
PICKING CARROTS. VERY GOOD, BOYS.
FETCH CRUNCHER, LOFTY.
EH?
WILL DO, SPIKE.
IT'S CRUNCHER, THE REGIMENTAL MASCOT.
MUNCH! CHOMP!
HE'S FOLLOWING THE TRAIL.

And the trail leads into the Colonel's office.
BUTT!
WAAAH!
OO-ECK! CRUNCHER NEVER CARED FOR COLONEL GRUMBLY.
AND THOSE PESKY CADETS ARE PINCHING THE COLONEL'S LUNCH.
CHOMP! NOSH! GOOD PLAN THAT.
Shortly—
GRRRRR! WHERE IS THAT IDIOT, CLOTT?
AHEM! MORE SURVIVAL TRAINING, BOYS, TO MAKE SURE THE COLONEL DOESN'T SPOT US.

BEDS of the SUPERSTARS
BAH! HERE COMES DAD TO READ ME A SOPPY FAIRY STORY!
CLICK!
FAIRY STORIES
BLARE!
BUT I CAN DROWN DAD OUT WITH MY ANTI-FAIRY STORY BED!
HEAVY METAL MUSIC NOISE
FAIRY STORIES
MY BED'S GREAT! BUT WHAT ABOUT THE OTHER DANDY STARS' BEDS? WELL, HERE THEY ARE...

ALARM
TICK
BURN
TICK
ZZZ
Desperate Dan's bed—
Bully Beef's bed—
JUST LIKE A BOXING RING, EH?
Smasher's bed—
I HAVE TO MAKE MY BED EVERY DAY, 'COS I SMASH MINE SLEEP-WALKING!
Bananaman's bed—
OUCH! I WISH BANANAS WEREN'T SO SLIPPERY!
BONK!
Finally, Vince Vampire's bed—
STRANGE HILL'S VAMPIRE PUPIL LIKES TO SLEEP UPSIDE DOWN!
SNORE!

(ALMOST) JACK and the BEANSTALK
THAT'S MY BONE YOU OLD TWERP!
AH, MY SON, JACK, HAS GONE TO MARKET TO SELL OUR COW. JACK HAS A GOOD EDUCATION, SO HE'LL HAVE GOT A GOOD PRICE FOR THE OLD COW.
YOU GOT MAGICAL BEANS FOR THE COW? NOT MONEY? BEANS!
I KNOW A BARGAIN WHEN I SEE ONE!
I'VE PLANTED THE MAGIC BEANS, NOW I'LL WATER THEM . . . I LEARNED TO DO THAT IN BIOLOGY CLASSES.
BOY! IS THIS GUY BORING!
MY GOODNESS! THE BEANS ARE GROWING ALREADY!
SUBTERRANEAN RUMBLE
THAT'S PRETTY HOT MAGIC!

NOW, IF MY THEORY IS CORRECT, A WEALTHY GIANT SHOULD LIVE AT THE TOP OF THIS BEANSTALK!
LESSER TWIT
BIGGER TWIT
I WASN'T WRONG. I'M SO GLAD I GOT A GOOD EDUCATION.
TO THE WEALTHY GIANT →
GREAT POST
ACCORDING TO LEGEND, I SHOULD FIND A HEN THAT LAYS GOLDEN EGGS.
MONSTER BROOM
MONSTER NIFF!
MONSTER SNAPPERS
HERE SHE IS. NOW TO LURE HER AWAY WITH A POCKETFUL OF GRAIN.
MONSTER CHOOK
IT'S WORKING!
HELP! MASTER! SOMEONE'S STEALING THE HEN!
TWANG! PLONK! DOING!
MONSTER TOENAIL
DASH IT! THE MAGIC HARP'S HARPING ON!

*And so ends our little tale, and Jack has egg — all over his face!*

The JOCKS and the GEORDIES
PULL HARDER!
COME ON! YOU CAN DO IT!
HEAVE!
JINGS! LOOK! A GEORDIE WHO CAN READ!
LIBRARY
LIBRARY
LOCAL LEGENDS
SHURRUP!
OYAH!
KLUNK!
LOCAL LEGENDS

OOH!
LISTEN TO THIS, LADS! ACCORDING TO A LOCAL LEGEND, EXCALIBUR, KING ARTHUR'S SWORD, IS BURIED SOMEWHERE NEAR HERE!
LOCAL LEGENDS
SO?
SO IF WE FIND IT, WE CAN RALLY ALL THE GEORDIES TO OUR SIDE— AND FLATTEN THE JOCKS!
Soon—
...SO IF THEY FIND EXCALIBUR, WE'RE DOOMED!
WE'VE GOT TO STOP 'EM! WE CAN'T TAKE ON ALL THE GEORDIES!
Shortly—
YOU SEARCH EAST— I'LL SEARCH WEST!
SO! THEY'RE USING METAL DETECTORS!

IT'S BLEEPING! I'VE FOUND METAL!
BLEEP! BLEEP!
BLAM!
CORRECT — JUST THE WRONG METAL! HO-HO!
OOH!
I'VE FOUND METAL, BURIED DEEP! BET IT'S THE SWORD!
BLEEP-BLEEP!
I'LL FIND THE SWORD — AND I'LL LEAD THE GEORDIE ARMY!

WHAT A HOOT! WE BURIED THE OTHER METAL DETECTOR IN THAT WORKMAN'S TRENCH!
HUH? WHAT'S THIS? ANOTHER METAL DETECTOR!
WHAT A MUG! HE DUG IT UP AGAIN!
THERE'S HUNDREDS OF SQUARE KILOMETRES TO SEARCH!
WE'LL NEVER FIND EXCALIBUR! WE'LL NEVER RALLY THE GEORDIES!
CORRECT! AND WHILE YOU'RE OUT-NUMBERED, WE'RE GOING TO GIVE YOU A BASHING!
OH, CRUMBS!
DON'T PANIC—

—FOR I HAVE THIS TOY SWORD, WRAPPED IN SILVER FOIL! IT'S SO REALISTIC, NOBODY BUT US WILL KNOW IT'S NOT EXCALIBUR!
EH?
TO ME, THE GEORDIES! FOR I HOLD EXCALIBUR! RALLY TO ME!
BUT THAT'S A LIE!
LET ME AT THE JOCK TWITS!
OI BE READY TO WALLOP THEM, OI BE!
HERE WE GO, HERE WE GO, HERE WE GO!
EEK! B — BLACK PUDDING BILL! CITY-GENT CYRIL! YOUNG FARMER FRED! SKINHEAD SID! WE'RE DOOMED!
B — BUT THAT'S NOT EXCALIBUR! IT'S — IT'S— ULP! THEY'RE NOT LISTENING!

BATTER THE JOCKS!
BIFF! BANG! WALLOP! THUD!
SMACK! BASH! BOOT! SCRATCH! SCRAPE!
OOYAH!
AARGH!
And—
GRR! THE ROTTEN GEORDIES CHEATED! BUT WE'LL GET OUR OWN BACK— LATER ON IN THIS BOOK!
GROAN! THAT SILVER FOIL SWORD FOILED US!

Strange Hill School
MY FIRST DAY AT STRANGE HILL SCHOOL WAS PRETTY FRIGHTENING, I CAN TELL YOU!
"It all started in a fairly normal way . . . ."
I'VE BEEN SENT A MAP OF THE ROUTE TO MY NEW SCHOOL, STRANGE HILL. WHAT A WINDING ROUTE!
"But then —"
I FLY TO SCHOOL IN A STRAIGHT LINE!
ERK! A VAMPIRE!
I M-MUST HAVE IMAGINED THAT! Y-YES, THAT'S IT! I'LL JUST FOLLOW THE MAP TO SCHOOL NOW.

"What a journey!"
A REAL SWINGER!
HAVE A HEART!!?
GHOULIE WOS HERE
TURN LEFT AT THE HANGING TREE!
YOU HEARD HIM! LEFT!
ME FOOT
DOWN TRODDEN SID
HE'S IN A HURRY!
FUME! BORED NUT-CASE
NOT GETTING AHEAD!
RATHER FINE THIGH BONE
MUMMY! THEY'RE ALL MONSTERS!
COMIN' FOR A DIP?
HE UNDERTAKES ANYTHING!
A DUCK CAN'T GET A QUIET PADDLE ANYWHERE!
DREAMING OF THROWING HIMSELF ON A NICE STEAK!
ABANDON HOPE ALL YE WHO ENTER HERE!

AH! THE NEW PUPIL! I'M THE HEAD! WELCOME TO STRANGE HILL.
A H-H-HEAD!
MEET YOUR CLASSMATES!
TREMBLE QUAKE CHATTER
I'M HAVING A NIGHTMARE — I HOPE!
OF COURSE, I'VE BEEN HERE SO LONG, NOTHING FRIGHTENS ME NOW!
AARGH! NO! NOT THAT! ANYTHING BUT THAT!
MORE TREMBLE QUAKE CHATTER!
GIVE'S A KISS, EDDIE!
MY COUSIN, CYNTHIA, HAS JOINED STRANGE HILL! SHE'S WORSE THAN THE MONSTERS!
HO-HO! SAP!

THE JOCKS AND THE GEORDIES
I'M THE HARDEST WORKER IN TOWN — I MAKE THE JOCKS' AND GEORDIES' FOOTWEAR!
TAP! TAP!
AND THEY WANT SOME VERY UNUSUAL DESIGNS!
PUSH!
TORPEDO SKIS.
THESE ONES ARE FOR LEAPING AT THE ENEMY.
EEK!
PYOIING!
OF COURSE, IT TAKES A BIT OF PRACTICE!
OOYAH!
THUD!

I DESIGNED BOOTS WITH PROTECTIVE STEEL TOE-CAPS.
DIDN'T FEEL IT!
STAMP!
BOXING GLOVE BIFF BOOTS.
THEN I MADE EXTRA-HEAVY TOE-CAP CRUNCHING BOOTS.
HOWL!
CRUNCH!
I DESIGNED A PATENT WATER SHOE...
SPLISH!
SPLOSH!
...THEN THE CROCODILE SKIN SHOE!
N-NO!
BANG!
NOW I'VE MADE A SPECIAL PAIR OF RUNNING SHOES —
CATAPULT SNOW SHOES.
CANNON PLATFORM SHOES.
BILL
— FOR ME! 'COS THEY HAVEN'T PAID THEIR BILLS! COME BACK HERE, YOU LITTLE WRETCHES!
N-NO FEAR!
RUN! WE'RE BROKE!

SPOTTED DICK
WHAT AM I, SPOTTED DICK, DOING IN THE HIGHLANDS OF SCOTLAND, YOU ASK? WELL, IT ALL STARTED YESTERDAY . . .
In my hospital ward —
FRESH AIR MAY CURE YOUR SPOTTYITIS — HAVE A HOLIDAY IN SCOTLAND.
So —
EDINBURGH
THE TRAIN NOW ARRIVING AT PLATFORM 4 HAS SPOTS!

WHAT BEAUTIFUL, CLEAR, FRESH HIGHLAND AIR!
UGH! WHAT A PONG!
PUTRID PONG!
WHAT CHEEK! THAT'S THE BEAUTIFUL SMELL OF SHEEP, LADDIE!
GOSH! THEY'RE FRIENDLY!
AYE! AND NOW THEY'RE SPOTTY TOO! YOU PEST!

BECAUSE OF THIS SCOTTISH AIR, I NO LONGER HAVE BLACK SPOTS —
OCH AYE!
— I'VE GOT TARTAN ONES!
SO HAVE I NOW!
OCH NO!
ULP! IT'S THE LOCH NESS MONSTER!
HO-HO! WE'LL REALLY GIVE THE TOURISTS A SIGHT TO REMEMBER!
G#*! *G#!
YOU READERS HAD BETTER MOVE ON QUICKLY BEFORE YOU CATCH SPOTTYITIS!

ALI HA-HA
and THE FORTY THIEVES
Ali's Dad is sergeant of the Baghdad bobbies. He spends his life chasing the forty thieves.
LOOK, ALI — I'VE CAPTURED MUSTAPHA NOZEJOBB, ONE OF THE FORTY THIEVES. AND IT IS ALL DUE TO FLASH, MY SPEEDY GT CAMEL.
WELL DONE, DAD. YOU'RE LUCKY TO HAVE A MAGNIFICENT BEAST LIKE FLASH!
COP SHOP
WANTED!!
MUSTAPHA NOZEJOBB
BANGERS AND CURRY LUNCH
MUSTAPHA NOZEJOBB
Proud to be a member of the force.
But—
HUH! ME AND MY BIG MOUTH! DAD'S GIVEN ME THE JOB OF LOOKING AFTER FLASH.
MUNCH!
NIBBLE!
Meanwhile, the world's most unhealthy bandit, Mustapha Phagg is plotting.
MICROWAVE
WE'LL MAKE A LITTLE TREAT TO SLOW DOWN THAT PESKY POLICE CAMEL.
CEMENT
FLOUR
GRAVEL
Shortly—
I SAY, MY DEAR CHAP — MAY ONE GIVE YOUR CAMEL A BUN?
BE MY GUEST! IT'LL SAVE ME FEEDING THE BRUTE.
ZZZ!

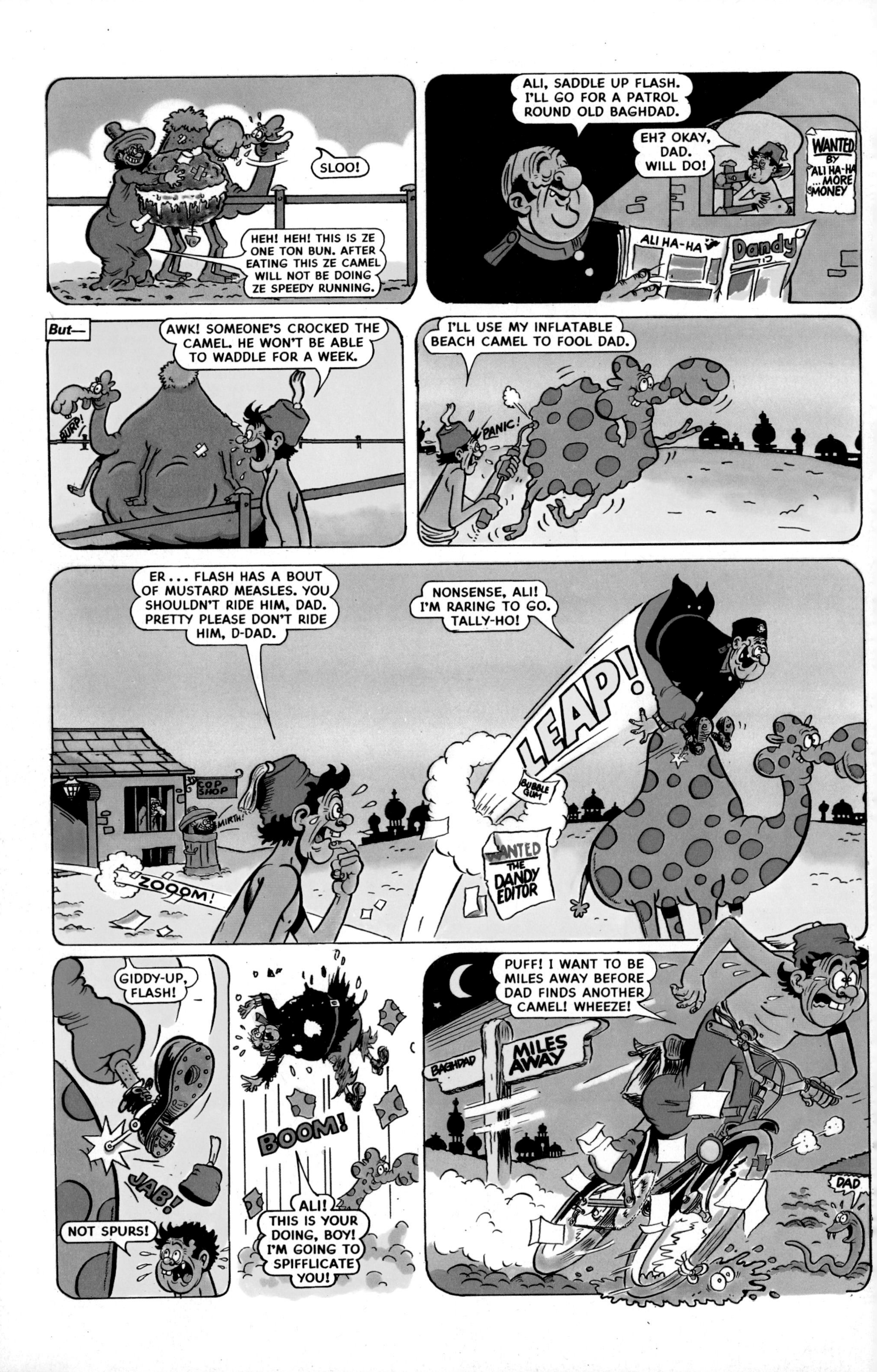
SLOO!
HEH! HEH! THIS IS ZE ONE TON BUN. AFTER EATING THIS ZE CAMEL WILL NOT BE DOING ZE SPEEDY RUNNING.
ALI, SADDLE UP FLASH. I'LL GO FOR A PATROL ROUND OLD BAGHDAD.
EH? OKAY, DAD. WILL DO!
WANTED BY ALI HA-HA ...MORE MONEY
ALI HA-HA
Dandy
But—
AWK! SOMEONE'S CROCKED THE CAMEL. HE WON'T BE ABLE TO WADDLE FOR A WEEK.
BURP!
I'LL USE MY INFLATABLE BEACH CAMEL TO FOOL DAD.
PANIC!
ER... FLASH HAS A BOUT OF MUSTARD MEASLES. YOU SHOULDN'T RIDE HIM, DAD. PRETTY PLEASE DON'T RIDE HIM, D-DAD.
NONSENSE, ALI! I'M RARING TO GO. TALLY-HO!
LEAP!
BUBBLE GUM
COP SHOP
MIRTH!
ZOOOM!
WANTED THE DANDY EDITOR
GIDDY-UP, FLASH!
JAB!
NOT SPURS!
BOOM!
ALI! THIS IS YOUR DOING, BOY! I'M GOING TO SPIFFLICATE YOU!
PUFF! I WANT TO BE MILES AWAY BEFORE DAD FINDS ANOTHER CAMEL! WHEEZE!
BAGHDAD
MILES AWAY
DAD

WINKER WATSON
During the school holidays six pupils remained at Greytowers Boarding School — and those boys included Winker Watson, the expert trickster, and Winker's pal, Tim Trott.
GOOD BALL, WINKER! . . . OH, NO! DAVE'S HEADED IT THROUGH CREEPY'S WINDOW!
"Creepy" was Mr Creep, the teacher who'd stayed behind with the boys . . .
. . . and he was having a hard time balancing the school's accounts.
Creepy put an instant stop to the game!
AS YOU BOYS BROKE MY CALCULATOR, YOU CAN DO THE SCHOOL ACCOUNTS AS A MATHS EXERCISE!
Winker set to work, and soon —
DONE IT, SIR! THE SCHOOL FUNDS ARE £100 SHORT! WHAT ABOUT OPENING THE SCHOOL TO THE PUBLIC TO RAISE THE CASH!
BRILLIANT IDEA, WATSON! BUT FIRST WE'LL HAVE TO CLEAN THE PLACE!
YOU AND YOUR BIG MOUTH, WINKER! CREEPY'S ORDERED US TO POLISH THE FLOORS!
CALM DOWN, TIM! I KNOW WHAT I'M DOING!

THAT WAS A GREAT IDEA USING A HORSE TO POLISH THE FLOOR, WINKER!
YEAH! HE'LL CHASE ROUND AFTER THAT CARROT TILL THE CHANDELIER STOPS SPINNING!
WE HAVE TO POLISH THE BRASS BUSTS, WINKER, NOT COVER THEM IN HONEY!
JUST FETCH THE SCHOOL CATS, TIM! THEY'LL POLISH THE BUSTS FOR US!
ALL THAT LICKING WILL SOON POLISH THE BUSTS!
EVERYTHING'S SPARKLING! WELL DONE, BOYS!
GREYTOWERS SCHOOL
NOW OPEN TO THE PUBLIC
THIS SHOULD ATTRACT THE CROWDS, SIR!
Shortly —
I HEAR ENGINES OUTSIDE! IT COULD BE TOURISTS ARRIVING TO SEE THE SCHOOL!
ER, DOESN'T SOUND LIKE CARS TO ME, SIR!

HOI! WE'VE COME FOR A TOUR ROUND YOUR POSH SCHOOL, MR FLATHEAD!
THE SCHOOL WE WENT TO HAD BARS ON THE WINDOWS!
ERK!
WE MUST HELP CREEPY, TIM!
THIS HAD BETTER BE GOOD, OR WE'LL CHUCK YOU IN THE RIVER!
Farther on —
WHAT A BORING DUMP!
ASSEMBLY HALL
YEAH! SHOW US SOMETHIN' INTERESTING OR WE'LL WRECK THE PLACE!
ER, THIS IS THE ASSEMBLY HALL!
IT'S AS GOOD A PLACE AS ANY TO THUMP YOU, GRANDAD!
GET 'EM, BOYS!
EH? WHO SAID THAT?

YIKE!
AAIEE!
JAB!

WHUMP!
TAKE THAT!
FLOUR
OUCH!

THAT'S GOT RID OF THOSE THUGS! WELL DONE, BOYS! BUT WE STILL NEED TO RAISE SOME CASH!
MIGHT I MAKE ANOTHER SUGGESTION, SIR!
CLEVER IDEA, WATSON!
VISIT THE SITE OF THE BATTLE OF GREYTOWERS
THIS SHOULD BRING IN THE PUNTERS, ER, I MEAN TOURISTS!
Soon—
AND IN THIS VERY HALL I DEFEATED SEVENTEEN THUGS WITH MY BARE HANDS!
MY BALL!
WHAP!
URRFF!!
THIS MUST BE PART OF THE TOUR! VERY FUNNY!
THE CASH IS ROLLING IN, TIM!
WINKER! YOU'RE A GENIUS!

Cuddles and Dimples
HELLO, FOLKS!
WE GOT LOTSA PETS! A RABBIT —
— A DOGGIE!
PING!
WHACK!
A CAT, A PARROT, A FISH, A FROGGIE, A MOUSE. AN' A SNAIL TOO!
POP!
BLOOMIN' PETS!
IF YOU MUST HAVE PETS, GET TINY LITTLE ONES!
ME GOT LITTLE PET.

SHRIEK!
ME GOT
A WASP!
BUZZZ
A
SPIDER!
SWAT!
H-
HELP!
OKAY!
GET CUTE
PETS!
CATERPILLARS
ARE CUTE!
BUT THEY EAT
A LOT!

PING!
AW! THEY TURN INTO BUTTERFLIES!

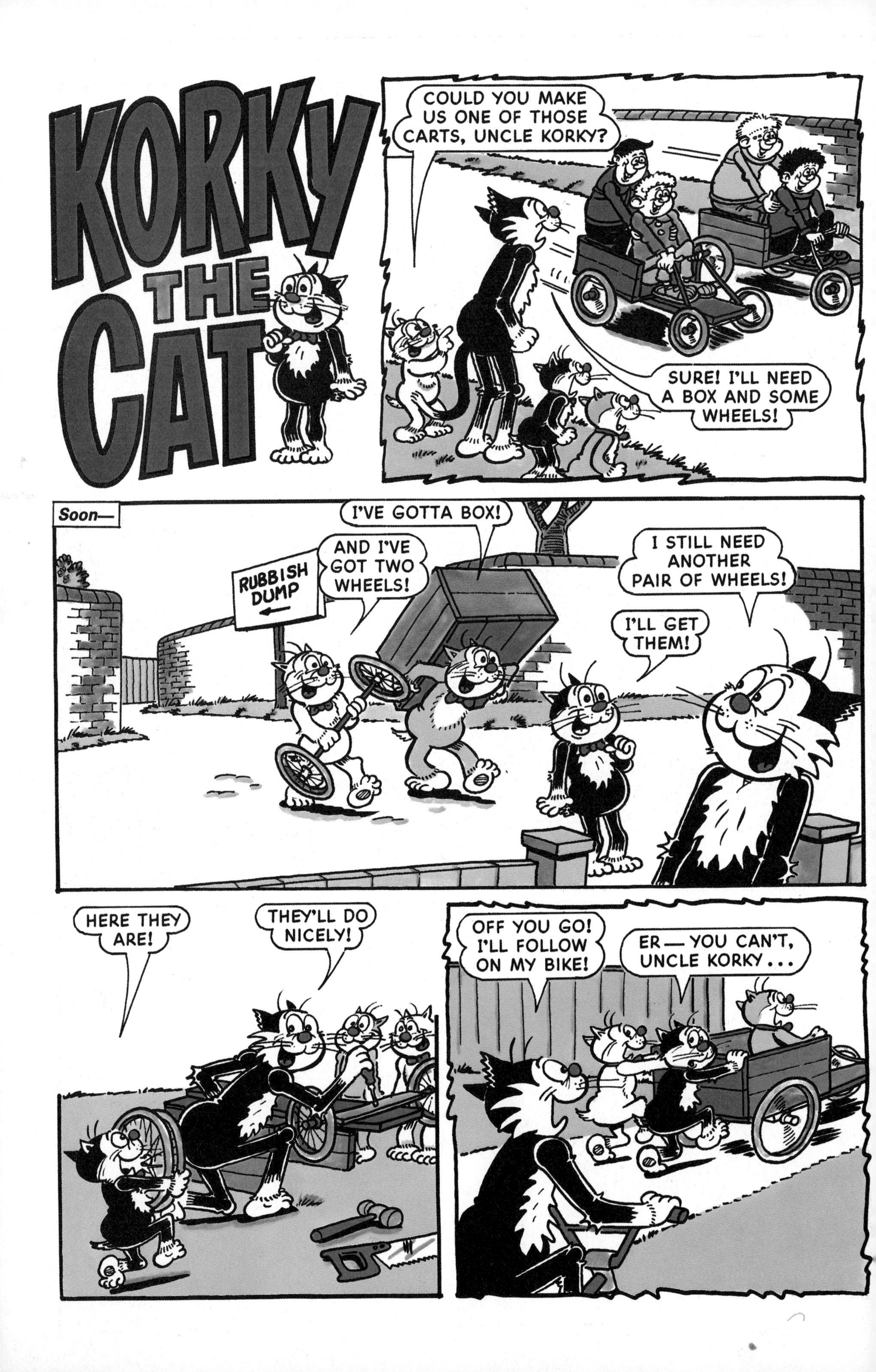
KORKY THE CAT
COULD YOU MAKE US ONE OF THOSE CARTS, UNCLE KORKY?
SURE! I'LL NEED A BOX AND SOME WHEELS!
Soon—
RUBBISH DUMP
I'VE GOTTA BOX!
AND I'VE GOT TWO WHEELS!
I STILL NEED ANOTHER PAIR OF WHEELS!
I'LL GET THEM!
HERE THEY ARE!
THEY'LL DO NICELY!
OFF YOU GO! I'LL FOLLOW ON MY BIKE!
ER— YOU CAN'T, UNCLE KORKY . . .

...THAT'S WHERE I GOT THE OTHER WHEELS FROM!
I SEE! WELL, I'LL JUST RIDE ON THE CART WITH YOU THEN!
So—
OUR CART'S FASTER THAN YOUR CARTS!
WALL COMIN' UP—TURN LEFT!
I'M NOT DRIVIN'—ARE YOU?
NOT ME!
I'M NOT!
THEN WHO IS?
N-NOBODY W-WAS!
BLATTER!
Later—
MY CHAIR'S FASTER THAN YOURS!
MINE'S FASTEST!
BET IT ISN'T!
GROAN! HERE WE GO AGAIN!

THE SMASHER
I'VE FOUND DAD'S OLD YO-YO! IT'S GREAT FUN!
I CAN SMASH WINDOWS!
PEST!
SMASH!
TINKLE!
YOU'RE FOREVER SMASHING THINGS!
NO, I'M NOT!
YOU ARE — I'LL PROVE IT!
I'VE COLLECTED A RECORD OF YOUR SMASHINGS!
GALLERY OF SHAME
THROB!

SEE? THESE ARE JUST SOME OF THE THINGS YOU'VE SMASHED!
Press Cuttings
SMASHER DOES IT AGAIN!
QUEEN DISGRACED BY SMASHER
SMASHER DEMOLISHES FLYOVER BRIDGE
A371 SFB
Miscellaneous Minor Smashes

GALLERY OF SHAME
EVERY DAY I'M GOING TO TAKE YOU IN THERE, TO REMIND YOU OF HOW CLUMSY YOU ARE!
BAH! I AM NOT CLUMSY!
I'LL TAKE THE CAR FOR A WASH.
SMASHER! WATCH WHAT YOU'RE DOING!
CRASH!
I DIDN'T LOOK WHERE I WAS GOING! I'VE SMASHED THE GALLERY!
CLUMSY, DAD! CLUMSY!
GALLER
SHAME

Mutt and Moggy
A GRINDSTONE — NOW THAT COULD BE USEFUL!
ONLY PURRFECT! NOW TO TEST THEM!
ZZZZT!
I KNOW I SHOULD LET . . .
SCHICK!
WAH!
. . . SLEEPIN' DOGS LIE, BUT I AIN'T GONNA! CACKLE!
THUD!
OOYAH! M-ME NOSE BONE!
GOTTIM! HOO, BOY! DID I GETTIM?
WOP! SCRAPE!
OW! ME BOTTY BITS!
SPIFFLICATION!
SCRAP YARD
WHIMPER! I W-WANT ME MUM — FETCH ME MUM!

SQUASHIFICATION!
NNYNGH!
SQUELCH!
HE'S AFTER ME, BUT I HAVE PLOTTED A CUNNIN' PLOT!
HERE I COME! HERE I COME! HERE I...
FLIP!
FLOP!
JUST LET HIM GO PAST— OLAY!
THEN A GENTLE NUDGE TO PUT HIM OFF BALANCE...
WHINE!
OH, MY...
SPLUTCH!
...GAWRSH!
YEP, GRINDSTONES CAN BE PRETTY USEFUL AT TIMES!
OH, MOAN! OH, GROAN!
HOSPITAL
TRUNDLE!

BANANAMAN
HI, FANS!
GOT HIM! CACKLE!
Doctor Gloom, a proper little villain.
WAIT UNTIL YOU SEE WHAT MY NEW RAY HAS DONE TO OLD BLUE PANTS.
A VILLAIN
JUST THEN! *
CLICK!
NUUK! WHAT'S HAPPENING TO ME?
*USELESS INFO'!!!

A FLAGPOLE
AAARRGH! MUMMY!
HEE! HEE! HEE! MY NEW RAY HAS MADE HIM AFRAID OF HEIGHTS.
SAVE ME!
IT TAKES FIVE SQUIRGLES A DAY TO BUILD A NIDDLE.
NOW TO RAID THE TELECOM TOWER. IT'S VERY HIGH SO BANANAMAN WILL BE AFRAID TO CHASE ME.
NASTY LITTLE WORM, STILL I CAN OUTSMART HIM...
TUM-TE-TUM TEEE-TUM!

READ The DANDY EVERY WEEK!
WITH SOME LOW FLYING!

AARGH! WHO PUT THE LIGHTS OUT?
POST
...AND HIS BLACK AND WHITE CAT. EARLY IN THE MORNING... TRA... LA... LA!
GOSH, THIS SACK IS HEAVY AND I HAVE TO DELIVER IT TO THE TOP OF TELECOM TOWER SO THAT THIS STORY WILL MAKE SENSE.
PHEW! AT LAST!
ZUMP!
OUCH!
FRITTERING BANANAS! IT'S GLOOM!
SCOOT FOR THE LOOT OR I SHOOT!
HELP!
THE LADY CALLED "MAY DAY" — THIS ISN'T YOUR PAY DAY.
OH, YEAH? WHY DON'T YOU TAKE A PEEK OUT OF THE WINDOW.
CRASH!
SHRIEK! I'M AWAY UP HIGH! HELP!
OH, NO! THE GREAT NELLIE HAS FAINTED.

FLY! FLY! FLY, YOU GREAT 'NANA — OR WE'RE BOTH DOOMED.
CAN'T! I'M HELPLESS WIV FEAR 'COS OF YOUR NASTY RAY.
SAY "AAH" AND I'LL GIVE YOU THE ANTIDOTE FOR MY NASTY RAY.
AAH . . .
. . . HA! YOU ARE NICKED, NAUGHTY BOY!
A THOUSAND CURSES! MY PLAN HAS GONE VERY WRONG!
YOU CAN'T LEAVE ME HERE! I'M A GENIUS! I DON'T LIKE IT! I WANT MY MUM! I'LL BE GOOD, HONEST!
POOR OLD GLOOM'S GOT A FEAR OF BEING LOCKED AWAY. WHAT A PITY, I DON'T THINK.
H.M. NICK

Rip
RIP the collie looked out over Rumstane valley. It was his own land and he knew every inch of it.
Suddenly a familiar and unwelcome sound reached his ears.
It was the Rumstane Hunt! The hounds had picked up the scent of a fox and were in full cry.
MOVE, YOU BRUTES!

Rip had not gone tar when a growling sound pulled him up.
It was the fox! Harried by the Hunt, the poor creature was exhausted.
Gently, Rip coaxed the fox to follow him.
The wise collie made for the river. Even hounds could not follow a trail across water.
The wild creature sensed he had found a friend. Working together, they moved a log into the stream.
Too tired to swim, the fox made full use of the makeshift canoe.
Downstream the fox leapt away, with a friendly yap of thanks to Rip.
Now the fox was safe, Rip could be on his way.

Tommy led Rip to his home, a lodge of Gray Estate, where they were met by the man from the Hunt!

SHH! I'LL BE BACK LATER!

Rip was very curious. What was Tommy up to?

Quietly Rip crept after his new found friend.

Tommy was visiting the fox Rip had helped earlier! The young lad was feeding the cubs.
I'LL NOT LET MY WICKED UNCLE, ALEX McNEISH, HARM YOU!

RIP! YOU FOLLOWED ME!

YOU TWO SEEM TO KNOW EACH OTHER.
The friendly animals rubbed noses.

Next day —
WE'LL GET THAT FOX TODAY — IT'S HOLED UP IN THE CRAGS!

Tommy had to save the foxes, and quickly!
I KNOW A SHORT-CUT!

When they reached the Crags, Rip barked a warning to the fox.
LUCKY FOR US YOU TWO UNDERSTAND EACH OTHER!

COME ON, WE'RE MOVING YOU OUT!

HURRY! I CAN HEAR THE HUNT HORNS!

They made for Woodly Cottage.
MISS GRANT WILL HIDE THE CUBS! SHE LIKES ANIMALS.

Miss Grant was delighted to help.
BUT WHAT'LL WE DO WITH THEIR MOTHER?

Then Rip barked for attention.
I THINK YOUR DOG HAS AN IDEA!

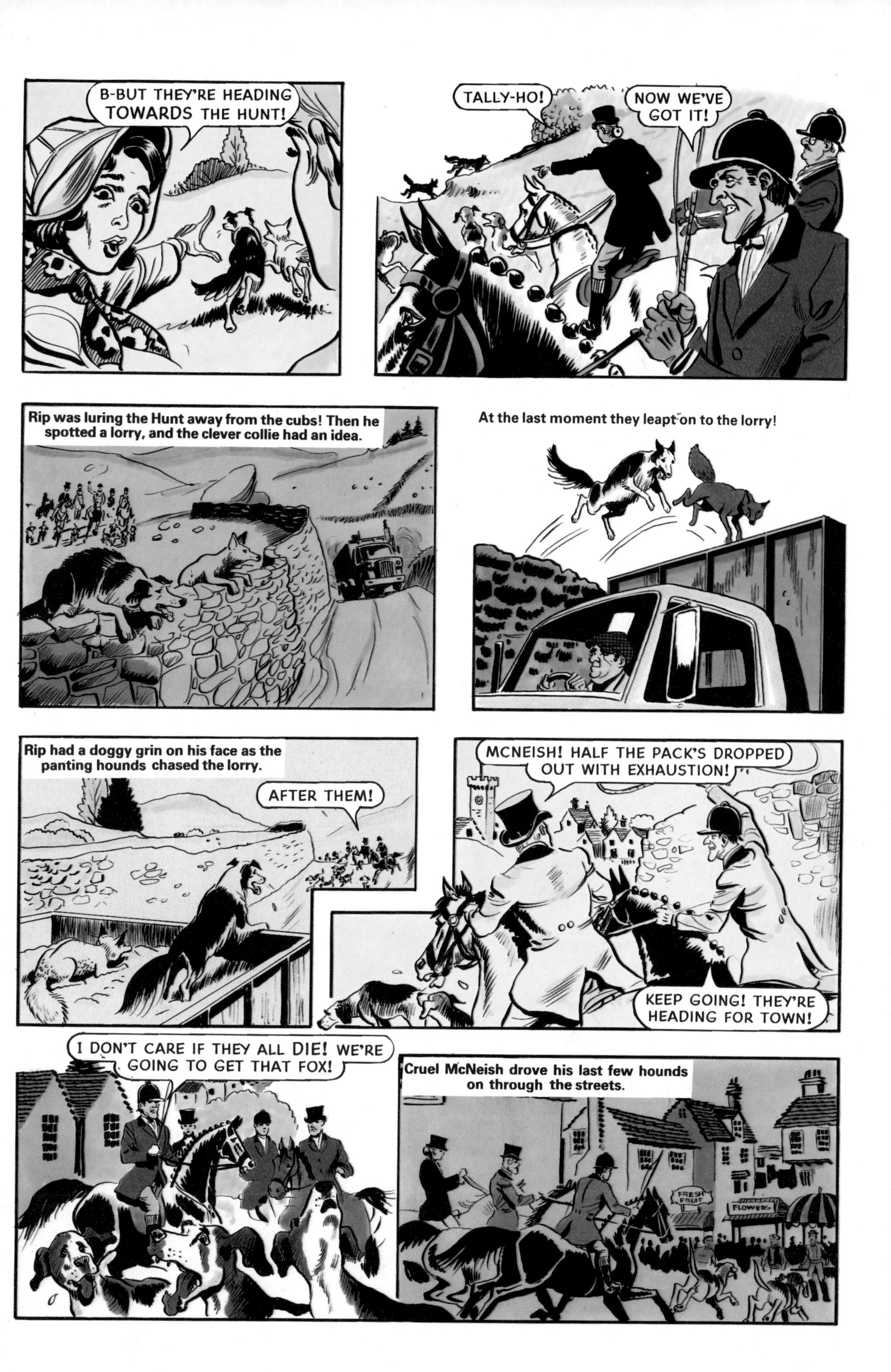
B-BUT THEY'RE HEADING TOWARDS THE HUNT!
TALLY-HO!
NOW WE'VE GOT IT!
Rip was luring the Hunt away from the cubs! Then he spotted a lorry, and the clever collie had an idea.
At the last moment they leapt on to the lorry!
Rip had a doggy grin on his face as the panting hounds chased the lorry.
AFTER THEM!
MCNEISH! HALF THE PACK'S DROPPED OUT WITH EXHAUSTION!
KEEP GOING! THEY'RE HEADING FOR TOWN!
I DON'T CARE IF THEY ALL DIE! WE'RE GOING TO GET THAT FOX!
Cruel McNeish drove his last few hounds on through the streets.
FRESH FRUIT
FLOWERS

Then disaster! As they chased Rip, the Hunt careered into the Market Square — right into the stalls!
FRESH FRUIT
AARGH!
CHEESES

OUT OF MY WAY, BLAST YOU!
THE RANT AND RAVE
FLOWERS
MY FRUIT!
YOU IDIOTS!
CHOICE
CHOICE

YOU—
THIS IS THAT LUNATIC McNEISH'S FAULT!
JUICY
CHOICE
WE'VE CORNERED THE FOX! MY LAST HOUND CAN HAVE HER!
Suddenly a snarling Rip appeared, leaping straight at McNeish! Plucking up her courage, the fox went for the startled hound.
WHAT? N-NO!

HELP! GET HIM OFF ME!
THAT'S HIM, OFFICER!
A VANDAL IN FANCY DRESS, EH?
Rip backed off. Now the police were here, McNeish would not bother them.
I'VE HAD ENOUGH OF YOUR RECKLESS ANTICS, MCNEISH! YOU'RE FIRED! AND I'LL SEE YOU NEVER WORK FOR ANOTHER HUNT AGAIN!
AND YOU'LL PAY A HEFTY FINE!
SERVES HIM RIGHT!

The foxes were saved, but Rip saw that Tommy was still not happy.
WITH YOUR UNCLE ALEX OUT OF A JOB, HE WON'T BE ABLE TO LOOK AFTER YOU ANY MORE, TOMMY . . .
. . . SO YOU CAN COME AND STAY WITH ME! I'LL LOOK AFTER YOU — AND YOUR BRAVE DOG, RIP!
YOU CAN? THAT'S GREAT! WHAT DO YOU SAY, RIP?
Rip yapped with delight! At last, the hobo collie had found a home, and a family to look after!

(ALMOST) CINDERELLA
CINDERELLA! HAVEN'T YOU IRONED MY DRESS YET?
AND WHAT ABOUT MY GOWN? HURRY UP!
YES, SISTERS! I'M GOING AS FAST AS I CAN!
TO THE PRINCE'S BALL, MATE! AND PUT THE FOOT DOWN, WE'RE LATE!
YES, YOUR UGLINESSES!
Meanwhile—
SOB-SOB! WHY CAN'T I GO TO THE BALL? SOB-SOB!
Suddenly—
PHATOOM!
YOU CAN, CINDERS, MY LUV! I'M YOUR FAIRY GODMOTHER AND I'LL MAKE YOU THE BELLE OF THE BALL.
SHOVE!

YOU ARE? YOU CAN?
OH-OH! I'VE PICKED A TOUGH JOB WITH THIS FACE!
S — SURE!
I'LL JUST TAKE A FEW MEASUREMENTS, CINDERELLA.
IF I MAKE HER PRETTY— I'LL HANG UP MY WAND!
NOW, WE NEED JUST A DROP OF FAIRY DUST — 28 KILOS SHOULD BE ENOUGH.
WHOOSH!
FLASH!*
TRANSFORMATION!
H — HOW DO I LOOK?
ER — UM — ER— DIFFERENT?
LOOK, LASS, JUST IN CASE ANYONE KNOWS YOUR UG — ER — FACE, WEAR THIS MASK.
WHAT A GOOD IDEA.
NO EXPENSE SPARED, LUV, YOUR TRANSPORT TO THE BALL AWAITS YOU—
—THE 29 BUS! BY THE WAY, MAKE SURE YOU'RE BACK HERE BY 12 O'CLOCK.
OKAY-DOKEY!

At the ball—
PRINCE CHARMING, HOW'S ABOUT A DANCE?
NEVER MIND HER— I'M YOUR TYPE!
SHEE! I'VE NEVER SEEN SO MANY UGLY DAMES!
EXCUSE ME, YOUR HIGHNESS, BUT ARE YOU FREE FOR A WALTZ?
GADZOOKS! A LADY OF MYSTERY!
FORSOOTH, BUT YOU ARE A BEAUTY BENEATH THAT MASK, I'LL WARRANT!
P — PRITHEE?
TAKE OFF YOUR MASK SO I CAN GAZE UPON THE FACE OF AN ANGEL!
IF YOU INSIST.
SURPRISED?
AAGH! I AM INDEED! WHAT A HORROR!
MIDNIGHT! I'LL HAVE TO GO — IT'S PAST MY BEDTIME!
OH, WOE IS ME!
And so—
ALL I HAVE OF MY PRINCE IS THIS SHOE HE LEFT BEHIND. I WILL SEARCH THE KINGDOM UNTIL I FIND THE FOOT IT FITS.
I HOPE SHE HAS A PASSPORT— HE'S IN OUTER MONGOLIA!

KORKY the CAT
CRUMBS! WHAT A NIGHT!
CRASH! BANG!
Next morning—
THAT WAS SOME STORM LAST NIGHT, UNCLE KORKY!
IT WASN'T SO BAD — THAT PUDDLE HARDLY COVERS YOUR PAWS.
YES, BUT I'M STANDIN' ON NIP AND RRIP!
WHAAAAT?
H-HE'S
RIGHT —
COME OUT OF
THERE, YOU LOT!
LET'S TAKE A WALK AND SEE WHAT OTHER DAMAGE THE STORM CAUSED, KITTENS.

AT LEAST OUR FAVOURITE SCRATCHING TREE'S . . .
. . . B—BEEN STRUCK BY LIGHTNING — SORRY, UNCLE KORKY!
OW!
CRACK!
WHUMP!
Later—
WELL, THE DAM ABOVE THE TOWN IS SAFE ANYWAY.
NO, IT ISN'T— LOOK!
IT'LL FLOOD THE TOWN — WHAT CAN WE DO?
THE ONLY THING WE CAN DO!
Soon—
THESE ARE FOR SAVING THE TOWN — YOUR UNCLE MUST BE PROUD OF YOU!
PROUD? YES! PLEASED? NO!
HE WAS THE KORKY WE KORKED THE DAM WITH!

Dinah Mo
I'M NOT BEATEN YET, MO!
OH, NO?
'BYEE!
ULK!
SPALOOSH!
Meanwhile—
MUM TOLD ME TO EXERCISE THE DOGS! SHE DIDN'T SAY ANYTHING ABOUT EXERCISING MYSELF!

NO, MO! DON'T . . .
SNIP!
WHO'S A LAZY BOY, THEN?
I'M HAVING A GREAT TIME TODAY!
WHUMFF!!
Then—
I FIRED AN ARROW IN THE AIR . . .
SWISH!

...AND THE PLANE LANDED... THERE!
OOF!
ZUNK!
BET YOU DIDN'T KNOW I LIKE PRESSING FLOWERS!
FREDDIE FLOWERS, THAT IS!
OUCH!
Back home—
HERE'S MY DAUGHTER NOW, OFFICER!
HI, DAD! I'VE BEEN PLAYING WITH MY DOLL'S PRAM, MY CRAFT SCISSORS, MY KNITTING AND MY FLOWER PRESS!
OBVIOUSLY YOU'RE NOT THE GIRL I'VE HAD ALL THE REPORTS ABOUT. SORRY TO BOTHER YOU!

Desperate DAN
I'VE NEVER BEEN THIS HIGH BEFORE! WONDER WHAT'S AT THE TOP OF THIS MOUNTAIN!
IT'S A WEIRD PLACE! I MUST MEET SOME OF THE LOCALS!
SHUCKS! YOU GUYS LOOK ODD!
DON'T BE ALARMED, STRANGER! WE WEAR GAS MASKS BECAUSE OF THE SMELL FROM...

PONG!
...KING PONG!
UGH! HE SURE IS SMELLY!
PONG!
THINK THAT'S BAD! JUST WAIT TILL...
ROAR!
...KING PONG BAWLS!
PHEW! THAT'S WHAT I CALL BAD BREATH!
I'LL BUILD SOMETHING TO FIX THAT HAIRY APE!
SCRAP YARD
WONDER WHAT HE'LL MAKE?
HAMMER!
BANG!
SCRAP YARD
BOOM!

BREATH SPRAY
ROLL-ON DEODORANT
THESE SHOULD STOP HIM SMELLING!
I LOVE TO GO A-WANDERING, UPON AN APE'S BEHIND...
BREATH SPRAY
SHUCKS! KING PONG DON'T SEEM TO LIKE MOUNTAINEERS!
GRAB!
ERK!
BREATH SPRAY
ROLL-ON DEODORANT

GASP! THIS GUY'S GOT AN IRON GRIP!
EH? I REALLY AM IN AN IRON GRIP!
I FOUND YOU SLEEP-WALKIN', DAN, SO I PICKED YOU UP TO TAKE YOU HOME!
SHUCKS! I WAS ONLY DREAMIN'!
FANCY DREAMIN' OF GIANT APES! AS IF THAT COULD REALLY HAPPEN!
CACTUSVILLE NEWS
GIANT APE SEEN IN CACTUSVILLE

Nasty Nursery Rhymes
HICKORY DICKORY DOCK, TWO MICE RAN UP THE CLOCK, THE CLOCK STRUCK ONE, AND I GOT THE OTHER ONE.
G#* *✡#!
OLD MOTHER HUBBARD, WENT TO THE CUPBOARD, TO GET HER POOR DOG A BONE. BUT WHEN SHE GOT THERE, THE CUPBOARD WAS BARE, 'COS I'D EATEN THE LOT!
LITTLE MISS MUFFET, SAT ON A TUFFET, EATING HER CURDS AN' WHEY, WHEN ALONG CAME A SPIDER, AND SAT DOWN BESIDE HER. AN' ME CLOBBERED IT, 'COS ME HATES SPIDERS!

AH-TISHOO!
RING-A-RING O' ROSES,
A POCKET FULL OF POSIES,
A-TISHOO! A-TISHOO!
I'M ALLERGIC TO FLOWERS!
BLARE!
RIDE A COCK HORSE TO BANBURY CROSS,
TO SEE A FINE LADY UPON A WHITE HORSE,
RINGS ON HER FINGERS AND BELLS ON HER TOES,
SHE SHALL HAVE MUSIC WHEREVER SHE GOES —
AN' SO DO I — HEAVY METAL!
HUMPTY DUMPTY SAT ON A WALL,
HUMPTY DUMPTY HAD A GREAT FALL,
ALL THE KING'S HORSES,
AND ALL THE KING'S MEN,
JOINED US FOR A BIG BREAKFAST.

THE SMASHER

OOH! AAH!
BOOT THE BALL BACK, SMASHER.
I'LL HEAD IT BACK.
SMASH!
SNARL!
I'LL HAVE TO RUN! OYAH! OYAH! OYAH!

COMIN' SKATEBOARDIN' WITH ME, SMASHER?
I'LL DO A HANDSTAND!
OH, NO! I'VE LOST CONTROL!
SMASH!
WAAH!
CRASH!
OOH!
BW
I MAY BE GOOD AT SMASHING THINGS —
BUT I CAN'T BREAK IN NEW SHOES!
PINCH!
SQUEEZE!
SHRINK!

THE JOCKS AND THE GEORDIES
ITCHING POWDER
STINK BOMBS
PEA-SHOOTERS
CATAPULTS
SOOT BOMBS
SWORDS
WATER PISTOLS
ARMOUR
GET 'EM!
SOOT BOMBS
SOOT BOMBS
STINK BOMBS
CHARGE!
PONG!
DO-IT-YOURSELF
CUT PRICES
BARGAINS GALORE
I'VE STARTED MY OWN BUSINESS, SIDNEY! ANY STUFF YOU NEED, JUST COME SEE ME.
TA!
LET'S START UP OUR OWN BUSINESS, AND REALLY FOOL THE JOCKS!
GREAT FUN!

USING ALL THIS STUFF, WE CAN CONVERT AN OLD SHED I KNOW OF! THIS IS A GREAT IDEA!
I ALMOST FEEL SORRY FOR THE JOCKS — ALMOST!
Later—
THOSE ROTTEN GEORDIES GAVE US A RIGHT DOIN' EARLIER IN THIS ANNUAL, BUT WE'LL GET 'EM YET!
TOO RIGHT!
DO-IT-YOURSELF GEORDIE BASHING SHOP
ARMOUR
SOOT BOMBS
WATER PISTOLS
CATTYS, CHEAP
CUDGELS
LOOK! JUST THE PLACE FOR US!
LET'S GO IN.
BOOBY-TRAPPED SATCHELS
PRODDING STICKS
SOOT BOMBS
STINK BOMBS
CAN I HELP YOU, SIR?
YES — HOW DOES THIS WORK?
ALLOW ME TO DEMONSTRATE. OBSERVE CLOSELY.
RIGHTO.

VERY EFFECTIVE, SIR, DON'T YOU THINK?
GROOCH!
WHAT IS THIS?
INSTANT TROUSER TERROR
I'LL SHOW YOU, SIR.
A LOVELY WEAPON, SIR, SELF-CHARGING.
HERE — TRY IT FOR YOURSELF!
YOU SEE, IT'S AN ELECTRIC EEL!

AAGH! HELP ME! OOH!
HUH?
GRAB!
HAWOO!
OOWAH!
LOOK — A NEW VERSION OF THE HIGHLAND FLING!
TRY THIS ARMOUR, SIR.
JUST THE JOB.
HERE — I'M TRAPPED!
SNAP!
SNAP!
THAT'S TRUE, AND TOTALLY HELPLESS!
ULP!
COME AND TRY OUR CROCODILE-SKIN BOVVER BOOTS, SIR — YOU HAVE TO SKIN 'EM YOURSELF!
SNAP!
SNAP!

OFF WITH THE DISGUISE, LADS! THIS IS A DO-IT-YOURSELF SHOP, FOR GEORDIES! DO-IT-YOURSELF JOCK BASHING! ANY LAST REQUESTS, MUGS?
BOMBS
BOMBS
POWDER
HAVE YOU SEEN MY DO-IT-YOURSELF DEMOLITION KIT?
WHAT?
A BUCKET OF HUNGRY WOODWORM!
BOMBS
POWDER
N — NO!
GRAB THEM WITH TWEEZERS, LADS! IT'S OUR ONLY CHANCE! CRUMBS! THIS WILL TAKE FOREVER!
MUNCH!
CHEW!
CHOMP!
CHOMP!
BLIMEY! THEY'RE EATING AWAY THE WALLS AT A RATE OF KNOTS!
NICE ONE, SANDY!

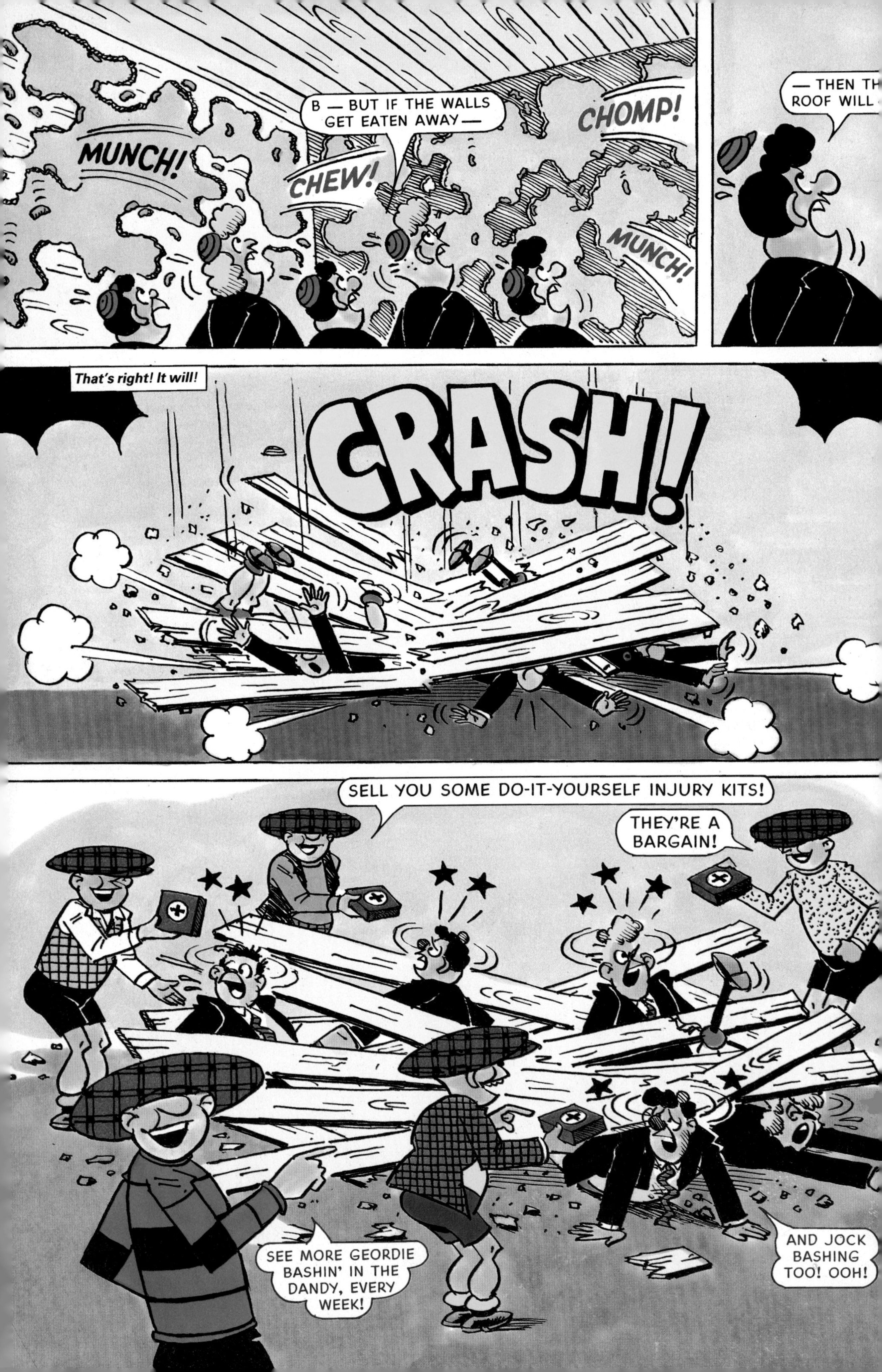

B — BUT IF THE WALLS GET EATEN AWAY —
MUNCH!
CHEW!
CHOMP!
MUNCH!
— THEN TH
ROOF WILL
That's right! It will!
CRASH!
SELL YOU SOME DO-IT-YOURSELF INJURY KITS!
THEY'RE A BARGAIN!
SEE MORE GEORDIE BASHIN' IN THE DANDY, EVERY WEEK!
AND JOCK BASHING TOO! OOH!

WHAT KATEY DID
GROWING UP IN THE WILD WEST IS MIGHTY TOUGH FOR A LITTLE GIRL. LET ME TELL YOU ABOUT KATEY.
THAT'S ME, FOLKS.
"Katey liked to play with toys. Only her teddy was a live bear cub and her rattle a rattlesnake."
RATTLE!
"I got the job of giving Ma Bear back her cub."
PAWS OFF, BUSTER!
BASH!
WAAAA! UNCA' DAN PINCH ME'S TEDDY!

"Every morning Katey and her pals would take their dollies for a walk."
OH-OH! IT'S 'EM BAD LITTLE INJUN BOYS. CIRCLE THE PRAMS, GIRLS.
SCALP THE DOLLIES!
"They were a tough bunch."
IS YOUR UNCLE DAN AT HOME, KATEY? I'M THE NEW SHERIFF.
I KNOW NOT TO SPEAK TO STRANGERS.
BUT I CAN MAKE A FACE AT 'EM!
STAB!

NOW THAT KATEY'S OLDER SHE'S A BIG HELP TO AUNT AGGIE.
THAT'S TRUE!
STAMP!
AND AUNT AGGIE SAID YOU'VE TO TAKE A BATH.
SPLASH!
HORSE TROUGH
HERE'S THE LOOFAH AND SOAP. NOW GIT WASHIN'!
SHE SURE IS QUITE A GAL!
SOAP
HORSE TROU

POISON
RATTLESNAKE ROLL
TAKE ONE LIVE RATTLESNAKE, COVER IT IN PASTRY, THEN BITE IT BEFORE IT BITES YOU!
I DON'T FANCY ANY OF THAT HORRIBLE FOOD! I BROUGHT A CHEESE AN' TOMATO SANDWICH!
BAT PIE
BAKE SIX CRICKET BATS AND THREE TABLE TENNIS BATS FOR AN HOUR- MY PET WOODWORM CAN'T GET ENOUGH!
DISH OF THE DAY
IF I ASKED NICELY, MAYBE IVY WOULD COOK EDDIE FOR MY LUNCH!
CHEESE AN' TOMATO! ERRGH! SOUNDS YEUCHY, EDDIE!

IVY'S REVOLTING RECIPES
JELLYFISH and CREAM
PUT A NICE BIG JELLYFISH IN A BOWL AND ADD CREAM- BUT NOT TOO MUCH CREAM OR THE JELLYFISH MIGHT SWIM AWAY!
EGG PHEW (NOT YOUNG)
FOR THIS FAMOUS EASTERN DISH YOU NEED 100 ROTTEN EGGS AND A CHINESE COOK WITH NO SENSE OF SMELL!
CENTIPEDE PUNCH
FOR THIS RECIPE YOU NEED 500 CENTIPEDE LEGS- IT'S A DRINK WITH A REAL KICK!
MUSHY BEES
THE PERFECT FOOD FOR A ROMANTIC MEAL! TAKE A HIVE OF BEES AND A FIVE TON WEIGHT! SERVE IT TO YOUR HONEY!
I OWE MY GOOD LOOKS TO IVY'S COOKING!
NO WONDER IT'S CALLED A SWEET TROLLEY! IT SURE IS DEE- LICIOUS!

WHAT GAVE YOU THE IDEA FOR THE PYRAMID, KITS?
WE JUST LOOKED OUTSIDE, UNCLE KORKY!
THE DANDY MODEL SET
YOU CAN HAVE THE DANDY FUN TEAM AT YOUR HOUSE EVERY WEEK...

...JUST ASK YOUR NEWSAGENT TO KEEP A COPY OF THE DANDY COMIC FOR YOU!

CRASH!
GOTCHA!